DESERT HARVEST

by

A. M. Merriweather

LUTTERWORTH PRESS
GUILDFORD AND LONDON

First published in Great Britain 1977

ISBN 0 7188 2329 x

Printed in Great Britain by
Ebenezer Baylis & Son Limited
The Trinity Press, Worcester, and London

CONTENTS

PREFACE

When it rains in the desert of Botswana after many months of drought, the people say with gladness in their hearts, '*Modimo o lekotse lehatse,*' which simply means, 'God has visited the land.' It is this that brings the harvest. The land changes almost overnight from brown, drab colours to green, bright hues and everything comes alive with hope.

So today Botswana is a changing country, full of hope for a bright future, even though war clouds gather on her borders.

This is the story of a family caught up in the changes. The names of the family group are fictitious, but the family is one that can be found in a hundred villages scattered up and down the vast land of Botswana. Thuto and his children give us a picture of family life in Botswana today: a picture of a changing people in a land of hope, a land surely harvested by God himself.

A. M. Merriweather
Scottish Livingstone Hospital
Molepolole, Botswana

I

THE FAMILY

IT WAS THE TIME of the year when the Bakwena had returned
home from their farms, bringing the harvest with them. The
farms were deserted, hut doors closed, cattle left to eat up the
mealie stalks and to manure the ground at the same time. It
was the happy time, the two months between harvest home
and the new rains which God would surely give as he had each
year since independence; the time for parties, for making
whoopee, for the repairing of broken down huts and rain-
destroyed walls, for smearing courtyards long neglected, for
the visiting of friends and gossiping, for attending church and
political meetings. It was the time for arranging marriages and
settling disputes; and also the time for attending clinics and the
hospital, for it could also be the sad period when epidemics of
measles, whooping cough and enteritis could sweep through
the crowded town carrying away little children, and when the
old people died of pneumonia and tuberculosis.

All through the chilly nights of late August and the gathering heat of September, ancient waggons drawn by twelve
yoke of oxen had creaked over rough tracks through the bush,
laden with sacks of sorghum, mealies and beans. Some people
had hired lorries with which to bring their crops and posses-
sions home. Waggons would soon be a thing of the past.
Blacksmith Jansen complained bitterly that nowadays if a
waggon broke down people no longer asked him to remake
the wheels with hard *mangato* wood; they just left the waggon
to rot away in sun and rain. All thoughts were now on trucks,
big five- and seven-tonners, Chevrolets, Fords and Bedfords;
bought, often second hand, in the Afrikaner towns of Zeerust
and Mafeking, just across the border. Thuto still owned a
waggon and his oxen were well trained. He and his family had
come home two weeks ago from their farm some thirty miles

north of Molepolole. Little Kabo had walked in front holding the guide reins. By the time they reached home his eight-year-old legs were weary and his body, naked save for a little triangle of cloth in front, was white with dust which hung in talcum clouds wherever anything moved at the end of the long dry winter. Thuto had walked part of the way, cracking his long whip over the backs of the straining oxen whilst for the rest of the journey he had sat in the front seat of the waggon, looking for all the world like the old Boer voor-trekkers of long ago who had first introduced ox-drawn waggons to Africa. His wife Mmapula had squatted uncomfortably on top of the bags of corn, her aged mother by her side. Dineo with her recently born baby lay covered with a blanket. Several other women and children had climbed on the waggon and had found a place amongst the hens, suitcases, sewing machine, chairs, ploughshares and buckets. Two or three skinny mongrel dogs trotted beside the waggon, darting off now and again into the bush in chase of a hare.

God had indeed been kind; he had not withheld the rains; the crops were good, the harvest plentiful, the people happy. A faint glow of light over the eastern hills towards Gaborone would soon give place to a red ball of fire as the early summer sun rose swiftly like a great balloon into the cloudless sky. In the semi-darkness of the round mud hut Mmapula threw off her blanket, rubbed her tousled greying hair and sat dozing on her goat skin mat for a few moments. Old Thuto, her husband of many years, had already pulled on his khaki shirt and trousers and was sitting outside in the courtyard on a low home-made chair before a wood fire. The now rising sun was warm and pleasant on his back. Soon he would move his chair into the shade.

'That is all men do,' Mmapula used to grumble, 'just sit and move their chairs with the shade as the sun moves across the sky.'

Mmapula was feeling her age and grunted as she pulled her tattered blouse over her naked body and climbed into her three petticoats, a flannel one, a print one and last of all her blue patterned outer skirt of strong material, typically sets-wana dress. She adjusted her headscarf, rolled up the mat, folded the blanket under which she and Thuto had slept and was ready to face the day. Beyond the centre pole of the hut her two youngest children were still asleep, their blanket pulled tight over their faces: Kabo her last born; and six-year-old Barongwa, his cousin, given to Mmapula by her niece who had long since lost herself in the teeming multitudes of the city of gold, Johannesburg, some three hundred miles away in the Boers' country.

It was eight years now since Kabo had arrived, her fifth child and only boy. Her womb never seemed to receive readily like so many other women who had eight or ten children. Only four of her children were alive, the first born having long since been taken by God. She had told Merri-weather several times at the hospital that she wanted another child, just one, another boy. Her womb was sick. He must wash it out so that she would bare a child and she and Thuto would be satisfied in their old age. But the doctor had merely smiled and said, 'No, Mother, you are getting old now; it is not womb trouble, it is your time to stop.' Even though she had retorted with some anger and scorn in her voice: 'Women older than I are still seeing the moon and bearing children,' he had merely said, 'Some women stop before others.' Eventually she despaired, believed him and resigned herself to having a mere five of a family and one was already in Heaven. In her heart she was grateful to God. Grateful also that Thuto was a good husband and father, whom they all respected and feared as head of the home. She remembered, of course, when he was younger he had neglected her now and again when other women took his fancy; but she had always remained quiet and patient, waiting for his return. He had never insulted her by mentioning the other women or parading them before her and she had never angered him by hinting that she had suspicions. After all she understood the ways of men; they were like that and she and the children had never gone hungry and he had always in public respected her. Indeed he had married her in

3

church and his father had paid eight cattle as bride price. It was a proper marriage and the whole village knew that. Her marriage certificate hung framed, next to her baptismal certificate, on the wall of the hut for all to see.

She came out of the hut, blinking in the face of the red sun. The two children, now awake, followed her, Kabo with his *tshega*, a little triangle of blue cloth, Barongwa with her *makabi*, a pretty skirt of beads. The children squatted on their haunches by the fire, their toes in the warm ash, a blanket across their shoulders. Mmapula greeted Thuto respectfully with a slight curtsy. She placed a three-legged black pot filled with water over the fire and, kneeling down, blew the dry wood into flame. The courtyard was clean, freshly smeared with a mixture of mud and cow dung. A low mud wall, irregular in places where last year's rain had caused damage, surrounded the home and at one place a little home-made wooden gate led out into the village. Beside this main hut, so neatly thatched and topped with a metal cone to keep out the rain, were two other huts, one similar to the large hut, but smaller, neat, well thatched, with two small, curtained windows, and the other at the back, dark and windowless, the thatch untidy as though it had been thrown carelessly over the rough rafters. A log of wood lay crossways a yard or so from the entrance, indicating that a confined woman was there.

The door of the neat hut opened and Mmapula's two teen-age daughters emerged. Serwalo was nineteen years old, attractive, tall, light in complexion, an enrolled nurse. Mosetsanagape was seventeen, darker in complexion with deep brown eyes, bright smile, intelligent, a student doing her Junior Certificate at the Kgari Sechele Secondary School. The girls greeted their parents respectfully with a slight bend of their knees. Mosetsanagape filled an enamel basin with warm water from the black pot, and the two returned to their hut. They were different in many ways from their parents, yet the home ties were strong. They laughed at many of the things their parents said and did and regarded their old-fashioned ways as quaint, yet they respected them and feared the stick

4

that old Thuto would not hesitate to use if he thought they showed disrespect. They threw off their shortie pyjamas and washed themselves from head to foot; they powdered their bodies, rubbed glycerine on their legs and skin-lightening lotion on their faces. Mosetsanagape put on her school uniform, white blouse and blue gym tunic, whilst Serwalo, who had a day off, wore jeans and a bright loosely fitting top. They made their divan beds and rejoined their parents at the fire.

Mmapula went into the hut and from a shelf neatly moulded in the mud wall took down a quarter pound packet of Joko tea, a sugar basin, a tin of condensed milk and a few cups and saucers. She brewed the tea in an enamel tea pot, added the condensed milk, poured out a cup and with knees bent in respect handed the cup on a tray to Thuto. He sugared it liberally and drank it slowly, carefully, with a smacking of the lips, as one would drink something precious, something tasty and good.

Mosetsanagape meanwhile helped her mother to make the delicious, sustaining *bogobe*, the tasty sorghum porridge, the staple diet of the Batswana. A paste was made of the flour, stamped and sifted from the sorghum grains the evening before by the children. As the paste was poured into the boiling water the porridge was stirred vigorously by Mosetsanagape with a large wooden spoon, her knees straight, her back bent double, the acrid smoke smarting her eyes. She had heard Thuto say with a twinkle in his eyes, 'A woman who gives her husband lumpy porridge is to be divorced'.

Thuto was handed his bowl of porridge first; he ate slowly with a wooden spoon. The children ate rapidly, Kabo and Barongwa sharing a basin. The sun was rising rapidly.

'It must be about 7.30,' thought Mosetsanagape, as she picked up her school case, balanced it on her head and walked quickly off to school, carriage erect. Kabo dressed himself in his school clothes, khaki shirt and trousers, pushed his slate pencil into his hair which gripped it firmly and ran off to the Canon Gordon Primary School. The others sat chatting

5

contentedly by the fire for a time. Mmapula sipped her tea slowly; Serwalo wandered off into the village to visit her friends, a large sun hat shading her face. She was conscious of admiring eyes upon her as she walked without haste, modern and educated.

In the third hut Dineo was suckling her child with her old grandmother by her side. She had given birth two months previously to a lovely baby boy. She would stay in confinement for three months and then emerge, fat, healthy and light in complexion. Mmapula took a huge bowl of thin porridge to her. She accepted it with both hands, and supped the tasty dish. Women in confinement do not use spoons and they must eat large amounts of food, frequently. Mmapula often quoted the proverb to her, 'A well grazed cow gives much milk'. The old granny rose slowly and painfully to her feet, pushing her aged bones upright with outstretched arms. She hobbled over to the fire, greeting her son-in-law Thuto, before she too sat down and enjoyed the precious tea.

Thuto rose; 'I must go to the kgotla,' he announced and walked through the little wooden gate into the village. The sun was now warm. A new day had dawned in Molepolole.

2

THUTO

THUTO WAS HIGH BORN, a junior headman in his own right and an elected member of the Kweneng Council: a traditionalist who knew custom and law and who was also an authority on tribal history and folklore. The chief relied upon him a great deal to help with cases in the kgotla. He made his way through the sprawling town to the chief's place, just as he had done for many years and just as his father and father's father had done before him. There were several cases to be heard and the chief might well need his help. First of all he passed by his own kgotla where several elderly men were sitting by the kgotla fire with the half circle kgotla stockade as shelter.

'Dumela, Rra Segametse,' called the elder of the two. He called Thuto by the name of his first born child, Segametse, the one whom God took some years ago. They had named her Segametse meaning 'the one who carries water' because the first born girl is quickly taught her duty of going to the well each day for water.

'Dumela, my comrade,' replied Thuto. 'Have you risen well?'

'I am well, father,' the old man intoned, 'just my kidneys are painful.' He placed his hands accurately over the site of the kidneys. 'And you, how have you risen?'

'I too have risen well,' replied Thuto, 'just the aches and pains of old age.' This series of greetings was repeated several times, slowly and politely, before Thuto reached his destination.

'It is only in places like Gaborone where people have no time, each to stop and greet the other,' mused Thuto. 'It is like a white town—that's not real Botswana.' The old man walked past low courtyard walls between groups of huts. People were sitting round their small fires drinking tea or eating *bogobe*. Lines of women and girls were going for water with buckets on their heads. It was easier for them now since the reticulation scheme had been commenced; pipes had been taken from the huge steel storage tank behind Khan's store to various points in the town where there were lines of taps. Thuto remembered how in the old days Mmapula might take half a day queueing up for a bucket of water at one of the few wells in the village.

School children, shiny faced with different coloured uniforms, were scurrying away to their respective primary schools. Pre-school children were playing happily in the sand, the girls building model huts, the boys making model oxen or little carts or trucks out of wire and sticks. Thuto passed the Grand National Café, a busy place, where local Chibuku beer, cool drinks, vegetables, bread, biscuits and tins of meat and fish were sold, and where one could sit at an enamel topped table for a meal of meat and rice. The ground outside the café was strewn with empty beer cartons and lemonade tins. A group of youths, unemployed, dressed in tight jeans and gaudy shirts were idling their time away and calling loudly to a line of buxom girls returning from the water taps. As the girls giggled and turned their heads the water spilled out of the buckets, running down their faces. A waggon came by, the oxen straining under the crack of the whip as they dragged a heavy load of firewood to the hospital for sale. A few women and children were perched precariously on top of the wood, waving happily to their friends.

Thuto reached the new tar road which began at the hospital gate and ran east through the town for a few miles. Here was danger, already one or two people had been injured on that bit of road where lorries rushed in and out from Gaborone. It was said that within two years there would be a tar road all the way to the capital. People said that Seretse's government had put these small stretches of tar macadam road in every major centre as an election gambit—in Serowe, Kanye, Mochudi, Mahalapye, Palapye and Maun, just before the elections of 1974. People said that this was an election gambit

8

to encourage them to vote Domkrag, to re-elect the Democratic Party. Thuto thought that strange because nearly 90% of the electorate would automatically vote for Seretse's party no matter what anyone said or did.

Everyone knew who Seretse was, the grandson of the great Chief Khama III. He was a chief, a big chief in his own right, and even though he had renounced the chieftainship of the Bangwato tribe his blood was still that of a chief! Thuto, like all his generation, revered the chieftainship. Furthermore, Seretse was well educated, progressive, modern in his outlook, an astute politician and a wealthy farmer to crown it all. No wonder both traditionalists and younger educated people voted for him. There was no one else of his stature in the land! Yet Thuto could understand why the Bangwaketse were divided and why many of them voted against Seretse's party. Their chief who had ruled them for many years had rather unexpectedly resigned from the chieftainship and gone into politics in opposition to Seretse. He was the leader of the National Front, the main opposition party. People said that it was out of jealousy that he had done that, for he was an older man than Seretse and according to custom was actually senior to him, just as Thuto's own chief was according to tradition the senior of all the eight chiefs. So when the Bangwaketse chief told his people to vote for him and his party it was hard to refuse. Many did refuse of course, because the vote was secret; one just went into a little wooden shelter and dropped a coloured disc into the tin of the party one voted for.

Thuto could also understand those Makalaka people around Francistown voting for their leader Matante who had founded the People's Party. This was just tribalism. There had always been hatred between the Bangwato rulers and their subservient Makalaka; and the Makalaka said that Seretse's uncle Tshekedi who ruled everyone with a rod of iron had been unfair and cruel to them. They never forgot that, even though Seretse spoke to them himself and called them his children and said, 'Let bygones be bygones and let us all be one nation.' Prejudice dies hard, although Thuto, listening to the election results on Radio Botswana, heard that the opposition party candidates had only scraped in by a narrow margin. The President had laughed and said, 'We nearly had a one-party state by popular vote; but a little opposition livens parliament.' Thuto did not really understand politics. He was glad that his chief and most of the Bakwena belonged to the Democratic Party, for he firmly believed that so long as President Sir Seretse Khama was in power things would be all right and the country would progress.

What really did puzzle Thuto was why Seretse, every four or five years, said, 'There will be another election'. When independence came in 1966, he like the majority of people had elected the Democratic Party as rulers and Sir Seretse Khama as President. Why should he be asked to vote again? He had already voted and stated his choice! That is why in the last election he and many others did not bother to vote. They had already voted! Perhaps the younger generation understood these things. Perhaps, as Serwalo and Mosetsanagape said, it might be good after some time to have a change of government. But Thuto knew that he would vote for Seretse till his dying day; after all, he was chief and a chief was god.

Musing thus with himself, the old man left the tar road and entered the chief's kgotla: a large open area of elevated ground enclosed by a huge stockade of ancient tree trunks. These had been collected far out in the veldt on the orders of the late chief Kgari Sechele. He had sent out regiments of men with ox waggons to cart the trees in, and they had been implanted, shorn off roots upwards, in a great circle. They were as hard as steel and afforded excellent protection against wind and sun. As he looked to the north, Thuto could see a multitude of huts and houses which made up a section of Molepolole and beyond these a broad valley with another large section of the town beyond. He could see the broad dirt road leading to this part, going past the burial ground where hundreds of mounds and a few grave stones marked burial places.

Thuto hoped that he himself would be buried at his cattle post, but he knew that nowadays most people were buried in the burial ground. People liked a good funeral as it allowed them to gather. He saw too, in the valley, the dry river bed which after rain became a raging torrent, and he remembered his friend, old Kgori, who a few months ago was leading a group of children across the river when he slipped and four of the children were swept away. Their bodies were not found for several days, but the chief's witch doctor had thrown his bones and said the bodies were buried in sand further down at a bend in the river, and that indeed is where they were found when the floods subsided.

Beyond was the endless bush stretching away to the north and west, a vast bushland in which the Bakwena had their farms and cattle posts, linked by innumerable footpaths and roads through the thorn scrub. Down from the kgotla he could see the new tar road shining like a snake, winding through the town, skirting the government offices, passing the Anglican church, the Kweneng Rural Development Association, the huge United Congregational church and the secondary school, to end at the stone gateway of the Scottish Livingstone Hospital. All this could be seen from the chief's kgotla, old and new together, but the new slowly and inexorably replacing the old. In a few more years this picturesque African village of round thatched huts would be a town of brick and iron-roofed buildings. No one wanted to build traditional huts any more; everyone's ambition was to build a modern house and an outside deep-pit latrine.

At one side of the kgotla stood the offices of the Kweneng Council where the Council Secretary, Treasurer and their staff worked, helped by a bearded young Peace Corps volunteer from America. At the opposite side of the kgotla was the Kweneng Council Chamber where the elected Council held its regular meetings. There were several one-and-a-half-ton Chevrolet trucks standing by the Council Chamber and Thuto saw that the Development Committee was in session. At the rear of the kgotla, facing north, was the Dutch styled house of the chief's residence which had been built by the British administration in 1935 for Chief Kgari Sechele II. The house was surrounded by a low mud wall, attractively decorated with different coloured muds and at the back was a huge smeared courtyard, hardened as though cemented, with numerous well thatched guest houses. There were always guests at the chief's place, for if strangers had nowhere to lodge they would never be turned away there.

When Chief Kgari was alive Thuto had several times been inside the house, for he and the late chief were great friends. Kgari was a real chief indeed; proud, angry, jealous, but kind hearted and generous at times. He always said that he would be the last of the great Bakwena chiefs. His people feared him, especially when he was on the bottle. 'Mind you,' Thuto used to say in admiration, 'he can hold his liquor like a real chief!' And when Merriweather used to tell him that the drink would kill him he would return storming to the kgotla and say to his men, 'I went to the hospital for medicine and all I got was a lecture on drink!' When he stood in the kgotla and shouted like a great bull his men trembled and even the witch doctors feared, for did he not claim to be the greatest witch of all? He loved the Bible, frequently quoting his favourite verse, 'Love God, honour the chief.' When he told his people to clear up the village, repair their courtyards, go to plough, come home with the harvest, go look for lost cattle, take their children for vaccination, everyone obeyed. When he told all the men of the tribe to give £2 to enlarge and renovate the London Missionary Society church, built in a similar way by his father Sebele II in 1907, they all obeyed. To disobey would cost a man an ox! And if he took his wife, a man would remain silent and shrug his shoulders, for was not every woman the chief's? The chief was god.

Thuto loved to sit in the lounge of the chief's home which his wife Gagoumakwe kept spotlessly clean. On the lounge wall in huge gilt frames were tinted photographs of the three great chiefs who went to Britain in 1895 to ask Queen Victoria to protect their country from the Boers and from Cecil Rhodes' company. 'There they were, the founders of modern Botswana,' Thuto used to tell his children; 'Sebele of the

Bakwena, Khama III of the Bangwato and Gaseitsiwe of the Bangwaketse.' These men it was, and their fathers, who welcomed the first missionaries, Robert Moffat and David Livingstone, Roger Price and Hepburn. They became Christians and tried to make their people Christian too. But most of the men remained as Thuto, uncommitted, 'just a person, not a believer' as the people said. Kgari loved his Scottish missionaries even though they did scold him about his drink and his women, and no doubt, thought Thuto, these things must have hastened his death on that visit to Swaziland in 1964. The Bakwena gave him a great funeral, laying him to rest in the chief's burial ground on the Molepolole hill. His prophecy came true, because there was deep division in the tribe over his successor and in 1966 independence came and with it the godlike power and autocratic rule of the chiefs waned under the new policy of government of the people by the people.

Kgari would never have settled down under that! God took him in time.

Chief Bonewamang was already settled in kgotla when Thuto arrived. He, with his clerk, headmen and councillors, was sitting on his home-made setswana chair in the shade of the kgotla fence. Thuto advanced slowly, knees bent, hat in hand, and greeted the chief by his tribal name *Mokwena*. A younger man rose and gave Thuto his chair; everyone knew who was his senior in the hierarchy of Bakwena life.

An old woman was being tried for witchcraft. She and the other women involved were sitting on the ground in front of the men. The headman of Masilwana ward had brought the case to the chief because he could not settle it himself; it was too involved. A month ago young Mpho woke up one morning to find her five-month-old baby badly burnt. Mpho had slept with her baby close to the fire as it had been a cold night. Mpho was convinced that the baby had been placed deliberately in the fire by a witch; she would not entertain a suggestion that the baby might have rolled into the fire; that would have implied carelessness.

'People have done it,' she said to her mother, not wishing to use directly the word witches. The local traditional doctor was called in to investigate. He knew the family well and he also knew that Mpho and her mother-in-law, Kabelo, were not on good terms. The family sat in a circle in the hut, quite a crowd, parents, relatives and close neighbours. The doctor put his divining bones to his lips and then cast them on the floor. Whilst everyone gazed fixedly, anxiously, at the bones, the doctor spoke to them rapidly, loudly, touching them and moving them here and there. He gathered them together again, put them to the baby's lips and once more threw them down. All eyes were on the bones and all ears were listening to what the doctor was saying. Then he looked serious and gave his diagnosis.

'This is no accident. This has been done deliberately. The child has been bewitched. Someone has a grudge against the mother, someone here in this hut. Someone facing Mpho now.'

All eyes turned to Kabelo the mother-in-law. Her wrinkled face contorted, her pupils dilated with fear. 'It is a lie!' she cried, 'those bones have lied! It is not I!'

The case dragged on for a couple of hours. The chief moved his chair with the moving shade. Many people spoke. Some said that they had known for long that Kabelo was a witch whilst others told of her dislike of her daughter-in-law. One woman had seen her one evening talking furtively to a witch-doctor, no doubt plotting her evil scheme. Thuto joined in, sometimes addressing the chief, when he used terms of great respect like 'great chief', 'man of the people'; while at other times he addressed the women, his tone changing as he called them 'children' or 'you women'.

At last the chief pronounced his verdict. Old Kabelo was guilty of practising witchcraft. In the old days she would have been thrown off the huge rocks above the cave of Lepolole. The chief ordered her to have two lashes and pay a fine of P20 as well as any hospital fees. Justice was done; punishment meted out. Peace came to the family and Mpho was satisfied, and forgave!

The next case was an easier one. Mosarwa was one of the many Makgalagadi people, who had over the past few years come in from the desert village of Letlhakeng to settle in a suburb of their own round the Indian shops and the mine recruiting organization area. Before 1935 many Bakwena lived there, and that is why the shops were there as well as the UCCSA Church and the Scottish Livingstone Hospital. The huts were on the whole of a poor shabby type, badly thatched. The area was noted for its drinking, its fights and its many radios and loudspeakers which played the so-called gumba gumba music day and night. Mosarwa's wife had patiently watched him going to the huts of his two girl friends for some months but she had remained silent until he had refused to buy her tea and sugar, and when he only returned home every second day for a few hours in a drunken state. She had remonstrated with him, not rudely for she was a quiet, reserved woman. His reply was to take a whip, which he had frequently used on her in the past, for after all a wife had to be kept in order and no one would quarrel with him for that; but this time in his drunken state he overdid the thrashing and the poor woman staggered two miles to the police station with deep weals across her face, neck and shoulders. The police had referred her case to the chief rather than make a case in the government court.

The councillors questioned Mosarwa and his wife carefully. They found that she had not been cheeky or disrespectful. Mosarwa had not even tried to hide his girl friends from her and furthermore he had used excessive force in his thrashing. The chief said, 'You Makgalagadi are a useless crowd, always giving us Bakwena trouble.' He ordered him to receive four lashes and to look after his wife in future. When his wife and the witnesses had gone, Mosarwa removed his shirt and lay face down in the kgotla. A tribal policeman stood at his feet and gave him four lashes, vertically down his back. The skin was torn, but Mosarwa made no sound as he rose, put on his shirt and said to the chief, 'Thank you, great chief'. He walked rather stiffly home, returned to his wife and in a few days when the wounds had healed took out a nine month contract on the gold mines.

The sun was now high overhead and the heat oppressive. A great thirst came over the chief. 'That is all for today, Bakwena,' he said, and his men dispersed. Thuto wandered off to visit his old friend Kgosietsile and sat with him chatting over a calabash of beer for a few hours. He arrived home in the late afternoon, the sun low in the west, and he found Mmapula busy with her sewing and the children stamping corn for the evening meal.

3

MMAPULA

MMAPULA HAD PASSED A busy but contented day. When
Thuto returned she was sitting in the late afternoon sunshine
on her goat skin mat with her old Singer sewing machine on
the ground in front of her. She was busy making a white confirmation dress for Mosetsanagape. She greeted her husband
respectfully.

'Greetings, father, how have you passed the day?'

'I have passed the day well, mother; and you, how have you
passed the day?'

'I also, father, have passed the day well.'

'It is just those Makgalagadi folk who give us so much
work,' grumbled the old man.

The traditionalist in him could not forget that those people
from the west were the hereditary servants of the Bakwena,
even though everyone knew that now it was 'one man—one
vote'.

Mosetsanagape was busy at the stamping block, banging
hard down into the wooden bowl with a huge pestle, her body
swaying rhythmically with each *thud, thud, thud.* She had a
good figure and she was graceful and full of youthful vigour.
The boys at school found her most attractive.

Serwalo had returned from visiting her friends in the village
and was busy ironing her white uniform with a flat iron
heated in the wood ash. She would have to be away early in
the morning to be on duty at 7.30.

Mmapula chatted away to her husband, one hand spinning
the wheel of the sewing machine. The fierce sun was low now
and the heat bearable. 'It has really been hot today,' she
grumbled. The sky had been a clear blue all day, no clouds to
give protection from the early October sun. There was real
heat in the sun now; heat that could call the early rain at any

time. Next month, surely, if God willed, the rain clouds would gather, each day packing higher and higher in the sky, and thicker. Lightning would flash all night in the far distance. Then one day there would be the noise of a great wind, vivid flashes of lightning would illuminate the whole sky, thunder would clap and the rain of early summer storms would pelt down.

Mmapula saw it all so vividly in her imagination as she sewed. Then the whole world would change—the brown, yellow colours of the parched earth would turn almost overnight to delicate greens and yellows, and little desert flowers would appear. Dry river beds would become angry streams of muddy turbulent water; dams would overflow and far out in the Kalahari salt pans would have a covering of water. The still winter hibernation would waken; flying ants would dash themselves in millions against the hurricane lanterns until, exhausted, they dropped their transparent wings and crawled slowly away to hide in the cosy earth. Butterflies of vivid hues would flitter with brilliantly coloured dragonflies over pools of water. Crickets would chirrup in the trees and in the veldt the fiercely beautiful orb-weaver spider, orange and brown, would sit motionless in the centre of its tough web spread between thorn bushes, growing fat with the myriad of tiny moths, flies and beetles that were caught in the strong, sticky mesh. Millions of tiny, active ants would follow each other in every direction. Frogs long dormant in the dry river beds would awake and croak all night long; birds, in love, would make their nests and the acacia trees turn yellow with blossom, whilst the rain lilies would burst into flower, their huge bulbs hidden in the sand. Far west the new-born antelopes would leap for joy and the young lion cubs, eager to learn, would follow their mother in the hunt.

The cruel things would also come: the snakes and scorpions and the huts struck by lightning sent through witchcraft by secret enemies. The hearts of the people would change also, hope would give place to doubts born of recurrent droughts, hope of ploughing and hope of harvest and food to eat. People would laugh—loud and happy laughter, and dancing they would cry, 'God has visited the earth; now we can plough!' Then the great exodus would begin. Waggons would be inspanned, loaded with seed of sorghum, maize, pumpkins, water melons, beans and lentils; boxes and suitcases packed; fowls tied together and thrown on the waggon; ploughshares, sewing machines, axes, spades and cooking pots—all were thrown on the waggon. The people who listened to the government agricultural officers or to the advice given over Radio Botswana would plough early with the first rains. Thuto always said that was dangerous because there was often a long drought between the early October rains and the heavy downpours of December. He liked to go out late in November, by which time the ground was well soaked and the cattle, having feasted on the fresh green grass, were strong enough to pull the plough. One day he would accept Mmapula's advice and hire a tractor as many people were doing; that was good because after a good rain one could plough a huge field in one day.

It was hard work for the whole family when the ploughing really started! They would start in the early morning and work nearly the whole day through, taking it in turns to guide the plough or drive the six oxen pulling it. There would be a break in the heat of the day for porridge and perhaps a cup of tea; no time for washing of clothes and bodies. Exhausted sleep would come, and then all hard at it until the field was finished. Seed was scattered by hand, melon seeds and pumpkins and beans mixed in with the sorghum. Maize sown in a separate patch. The big farmers—and there were many of them now—did not interest Thuto very much, for he was too fixed in his ways. They ploughed huge areas of land, using tractors, planters, fertilizers, and now with new legislation they were to be allowed to fence their land. Chief Kgari would never have agreed to that!

Once she moved out to her lands Mmapula knew that she would be there, on and off, for nine months. After ploughing and sowing, if the rains came well, there was the hand-blistering work of hoeing, getting rid of the grass and weeds which would choke the corn. She used to hear her father say when the heavy rains of January and February came, 'Now the women will really have to get down to hard work.' After the hoeing, if the rains had been good, there would be water melons and she and the family would sit in the shade of the hut, slice a huge melon in half and she would say, 'Let us drink water melon.' Then they would scoop out the refreshing fruit with their fingers.

Soon the cooler months would come; the beans would ripen, then the maize, pumpkins, cane sugar, and last of all the sorghum. There would be long days walking up and down the fields, shouting until one was hoarse, clapping hands to drive away the flocks of hungry birds which could take half a lazy woman's field of corn in a day. Sometimes pests would come, like the corn-crakes, *stotojanes*, horrible, fat bellied, horny, long legged creatures which could come in their thousands, crawling everywhere to eat the crops. They were nearly as bad as the locusts of the old days before the white people wiped them out,—except that locusts could be eaten; no one could eat stotojanes! In late June, July and August came the main harvest, the proper food. The sorghum would be gathered in, each head of corn cut off separately from the stem, then packed on wooden trestles off the ground. The grains would be frosted white in the bitter winter nights. Then the threshing floor would be smeared with mud and hardened by the sun, the heads of corn piled in the centre and the women, each with a heavy stick, would go round and round, singing as they went, beating the heads of corn. But a pregnant woman must not go on the threshing floor—that would bring bad luck. Then the winnowing, the chaff blown away by the August winds; the precious, tiny seeds of sorghum then packed into sacks or home-made grass storage bins. The end of August and home again.

The cycle had gone on for as long as she could remember. Mmapula of course had her visits home during these nine months; monthly she came for Holy Communion. Her church membership card did not show an absent month. She came home for Christmas, for she loved the nativity play performed year after year by the young people. It never changed —Mary sweeping the floor, startled by the angel's visit; Joseph always making a wooden table; the terrified shepherds whose antics always brought laughter; and what every one always waited for, the anger of Herod at the appearance of the wise men. And she would go home to buy sugar and tea, and for funerals; a thirty mile walk there and back did not worry her; it was nice to go home, see her friends and the folk at church and have a gossip in the shops.

She never forgot those years of drought: those long years before independence, when for three years there was hardly any rain, no ploughing, people simply living on mealie meal porridge and on the grain sent from America and Britain. Some of the ministers and church leaders said God was very angry, that it was his punishment for the things the politicians were saying. There was hate in the land and people were afraid of independence. There was an upsurge of so-called prophets; men who claimed healing power from God, who baptized saying their baptism was far greater and more wonderful than any baptism that the ordinary church leaders could give, for it not only gave forgiveness of sin but it healed body and spirit; who tied coloured cords round the necks and loins of their followers and hung little bottles of holy water round their followers' necks. All for money, big money. Some people said that it was these people who had angered God, by making money out of the Bible; others said it was because people were sinning and not going to church. No one knew: only that God in anger kept back the rains and hunger came.

The chief called the people to the kgotla for special prayers for rain. Great crowds went, all the different ministers and the prophets and the witch doctors too. Church leaders preached fiery sermons, quoting texts from the Old Testament which promised rain if God's people would only repent. Not only men prayed but women also were called upon to pray. Women knew how to pray, how to flatter and honour God and plead with him, using language which would surely soften the heart of an angry, righteous God. Mmapula well remembered old Molemi's prayer. That woman could pray if anyone could!

> God of our fathers, of Abraham, Isaac and Jacob,
> God without beginning and without end,
> God who is holy and righteous, yet is full of love and mercy,
> God who can forgive, forgive us, Oh God!
> Look at the scorched earth, dressed as it is in yellow
> Like a lion.
> Hear the silence of the land, merciful Father;
> No frogs croak, no crickets sing, no birds sing for joy,
> The springbok in the Kalahari no longer leap and dance;
> Their little ones die.
> Your people are hungry, God who has all power.
> They have ploughed in vain and returned home in despair,
> Their hearts are dead, their little children hungry.
> They say, 'Why is God so angry?'
> Open your heavens, O Lord God almighty,
> Send down the gentle female rain, merciful Father,
> The gentle, penetrating rain, the soaking rain.
> Let your people plough, O God!
> Send not the rain with lightning that kills.
> Have mercy upon us, O loving God, and we shall eat, live and
>   praise you.
> Forgive and save us
> For your only Son's sake.
> Amen.

And the great congregation echoed Amen.

But the drought continued all through the year of independence. People said that after Seretse was made President God would hear. On September 30, 1966 a terrible wind blew across from the Transvaal. The sky was red with dust; dust sent by the Transvaal Boers who did not want our independence. Midnight came, the wind howled, dust filled people's eyes and choked them. In Gaborone Sir Seretse Khama walked out to the flag staff with the British High Commissioner. The representatives of the nations of the world were watching. Princess Marina and Lady Khama huddled together in the stadium, the wind howling round them. The Union Jack was hauled slowly down and Sir Seretse raised the Botswana flag— blue to represent the blue skies which give the rain, a black band across to represent the black people and two thin white bands to represent the whites—the only flag in Africa which has anything to represent the white dwellers in the land! The wind tore at it as if trying to carry it away, and in Molepolole, Kanye, Serowe and a dozen other villages the flag rose in the tearing wind; it rose announcing proudly the birth of another nation. The next day the wind dropped, the showers came and the President smiled, for the chief, since ancient times, was the rain maker! The people and the land smiled. The drought was over, years of rain, blessing and progress had begun.

Mmapula thought of all these things as she sat sewing in her courtyard with a new rainy season approaching. Then she came out of her reverie and, still working at the dress, told Thuto of her day.

When Thuto had left for the kgotla Mmapula had decided to walk over to the Indian shop before the heat of the day became too oppressive. The sugar was finished, only a few teaspoon- fuls of tea left and she wanted another yard of white material for Mosetsanagape's dress. She washed herself, tidied her blouse and headscarf, put on her home-made sandals and set off in the opposite direction to Thuto for Jalal's shop. There were at least six Indian trading stores in the village as well as a Co-operative store, numerous cafés and other shops with 'restricted dealers' licences'. A chemist shop had also just been opened. She preferred Jalal's shop, not because it was any cheaper than the others, but because it was nearer, and she always met some of her friends there. If she heard that sugar was a cent cheaper at Moorad's or Khan's stores she would go there. She was good at shopping around! She too headed for the tar road, but progress was slow, for she met numerous people with whom she exchanged the traditional, slow, un- hurried greetings of the day. The smooth tar road was kind to her feet, but when she drew near to Mokone's café she saw a crowd of young men and women who, although the day was still young, had been drinking and were dancing and shouting. She skirted across the bush behind the café muttering to herself, 'No one is safe these days, people are always being stabbed and robbed'.

She walked past the offices of the Mine Recruiting Organization where a crowd of young men were standing waiting to offer their services for work on the Gold Mines of Johannesburg. This was recruiting day and they would be registered, examined by the doctor and next day they would start off on the 300 mile road and rail journey to Johannesburg. They would toil far below ground, digging out the precious metal, for contracts of nine months. They would send money home to wives and parents and they would return themselves in due course, strong, muscular and hungry for the sight and smell of home.

Thuto had gone to the mines several times in his younger days. He started soon after their marriage when he was sure Mmapula was pregnant, and he returned nine months later to take her out of confinement. In those early days of marriage he never really liked to leave her until he was sure she was pregnant, for there were always 'thieves' around and women were such gullible things, easily led astray.

Mmapula could see that some of the recruits were Makgalagadi from far out in the desert. Others were just youngsters, tired of herding goats and cattle. They wanted money and the thrill of a big city. Others had quarrelled with their parents and were running away. Some would be rejected by the doctor. He would put his stethoscope on a man's chest and say, 'I must reject him, his lungs are defective,' or, 'You are too young, you have no wisdom teeth, come back next year.' But most would go and then when the money came home, wives and mothers would buy sugar, salt, tea, powdered milk and, when the rains came, seed for sowing.

Slowly and carefully she extracted a ten pula note from her head square where she had carefully tied it in one corner. Last week Thuto had sold a goat to butcher Ishmael, a big, fat one which had realized fourteen pula. Only a couple of years ago such an animal would have brought in six pula or less. But everything was changing, not only the hearts of people, not only the ways of young people, but prices: weekly they were rising; even Joko tea and sugar had risen in price recently. Mmapula had not heard of inflation which in its worldwide greed had engulfed South Africa whose economy was intimately related to Botswana's. She thought the increased prices were due to the greedy traders putting their heads together and increasing prices all round. She counted the change carefully which Mr. Jalal handed over to her and in her mind she still called a one pula note ten shillings, and the little thebe copper coin a penny. Yet that sterling money had long since gone out of use; long before independence the currency had switched over to the South African rand and cent; a rand was at that time equivalent to a ten shilling note. All one had to do was to divide the rands by two and one got back to pounds. Through all these years she and her generation had said that they could not understand rands and cents. The proper Setswana language was pounds and pence. In church when the minister announced the collection as so many rands and cents, old Khumoyakgosi always stood up and said, 'Put that into setswana so that we can understand.' He meant, put it into pounds and pence, and so the minister, ignoring any devaluation of the pound over these last fifteen years or so, would divide by two. Then Khumoyakgosi and his generation would be happy and say, 'Thank you, now we know where we are.'

But over a year ago the President himself had come to Molepolole and at a great meeting, crowded with men and women, he had made a great speech, in beautiful setswana with lots of idioms and proverbs, in which he had promised that soon Botswana would have her own currency; no longer would we use South African money, we would have our own; a rand would be called a pula and a cent a thebe. His promise was fulfilled on August 23, 1976, when the new currency appeared. Pula notes and thebe coins, bearing the President's picture! All could see that this was Botswana's own currency, quite different from rands and cents, and it even made one forget the old money of pounds and shillings. The Government said that all should take their rands and cents and even their pounds and change them into the new Botswana currency. August 23 was ever after to be called Pula day. People flocked in their thousands to change their money and some, like old Masilonyane, dug up the floor of his hut where years ago he had hidden in a tin box over a thousand pound notes and a few gold sovereigns. He would never have changed these into rands but he had no hesitation in changing them into Seretse's money! To have its own currency made a nation proud. This was another of Seretse's triumphs! Mmapula still wondered what all this change of money was about and she wondered if she would ever understand, but as she said to her children, 'This is our own Botswana money, I really must try to understand it and forget about pounds and shillings.'

Mmapula now changed into an old print dress and commenced an hour or two of smearing. She was repairing the mud wall of the courtyard where the previous rains had washed pieces of the wall away. She felt irritable because Serwalo had not yet returned. 'She ought to have spent the day helping me here,' thought the old lady, 'rather than wandering about the town.' It was so hard: one sacrifices and educates one's children and then they despise the proper work of women: hoeing, smearing and going for water. She smeared the walls with a mixture of mud and cow dung. Yesterday she had smeared the courtyard, making attractive patterns with her fingers as she finished the top layer of cow dung. People would see that Thuto's wife was no lazy woman! By the time Thuto returned she had finished the wall and was busy at Mosetsanagape's dress; Serwalo had returned and gone off for water; while Kabo was milking the few goats his father kept at home for milk.

As the sun set over the far Kalahari horizon, the family sat together around the courtyard fire. There were beans in a small three-legged pot which Serwalo was cooking and there was porridge in a larger pot and water in a third. The meal was cooked and eaten leisurely, the girls helping their mother, quite used to the constant back-bending and the wood smoke in their eyes. Thuto was served first. He shared the beans with Serwalo whilst the others ate porridge. After they had eaten Thuto talked a good deal, telling them tales of old days and stories about animals and snakes. He spoke of the Boer traders who used to be in Molepolole and who disappeared with the coming of independence, and of the chiefs, Sebele and Kealeboga, of how they stamped their feet when angry and the whole tribe trembled! He would tell of tribal wars and history, and his folk stories held the children spellbound. And animals too; he would tell of the customs of lions, snakes and baboons. 'When you see lots of rock rabbits, look for pythons,' he would warn his children. Little Kabo trembled when his father told how a python would crush its victim, then lick him all over to make him slimy before swallowing him feet first until only the head was left hanging out of the snake's mouth! If its victim was an antelope, just when the horns were left sticking out brave people would rush up to the now tired snake and stamp on its belly, pushing the antelope back out of the snake's mouth so that they could take it away and eat it themselves! He would tell of the baboons which shared the rocky hills with pythons and leopards. 'Oh, such sensitive creatures they are,' he would tell his youngsters. 'It you point a gun at them they will become almost human, whimpering and praying for you not to fire; or they will fall down dead with fright. They love to eat scorpions, hunting for them under rocks. They will lift big rocks up very carefully and slowly, peeping underneath for the scorpions. If they find a snake there instead they will look the other way and then slowly place the rock back where it was. But when they find a scorpion they do not fear its wicked sting, but pop it live in their mouths moving it from side to side, seemingly to enjoy its vicious sting before chewing it!'

The moon rose crescent in the west; the evening star Venus looked benignly down: 'asking for supper' was its name. All over the land families were sitting round the evening fires.

Soon after 9 p.m. Mmapula yawned and said, 'It is time to retire, let us have a prayer before we sleep'. She was a sincere Christian and liked to pray long earnest prayers, full of idioms and proverbs. Thuto did not mind that. He appreciated good oratory and a Christian wife was usually a good one. He did not mind her going off to church on Sundays and asking for collections for this and that. She knelt down by the fire, a child before her great Father in heaven.

She poured out her heart in gratitude to him, thanking him for his protection and care through another day. Her lined face was full of peace and contentment. She prayed for Thuto and the children and for her church and minister and for the sick. She prayed especially that soon the rains would come. She said, 'Soon we shall be asleep, it will appear that our spirits have left our bodies travelling we know not where. Bring them back so that we can arise refreshed in the morning.' She prayed for his protection through the night with all its dangers. She did not mention witches but that is what she meant by the 'dangers of the night'. She and the little ones went to bed first: Serwalo and Mosetsanagape took a basin of water and retired to their hut. Thuto sat awhile watching the dying embers of the fire before joining his wife on the goat skin mat.

In the village all was quiet now. A woman in labour walked slowly up the road to the hospital, mother and sister walking with her, hurricane lantern lit. An occasional lorry passed to Gaborone. The late drinkers from the cafés staggered home. Lovers met at pre-arranged places. Respectable people did not go out now. *Baloi* would be around, evil came with the night: owls and snakes and witches; and young people disobedient.

When she was sure that her parents were asleep Serwalo slipped out of the hut. Every girl of her age had a boyfriend and she would be back by first light. Mosetsanagape would never tell on her.

4

DINEO

MMAPULA SPENT AS MUCH time as possible with Dineo and
her baby in the small hut behind the main living hut. It could
be quite lonely spending three months in confinement,
although it was a happy, restful time on the whole, with
numerous female visitors. Mmapula had never forgotten the
tragedy of her firstborn daughter, Segametse, 'the one who
goes for water'. Everyone called her Mma-Segametse and
Thuto Rra-Segametse, as custom decreed, but the name
always gave her a twinge of pain because Segametse's death
had been long, painful and probably unnecessary.

Segametse had told her mother that the nurses at the clinic
had advised her to stay at home in her last month of pregnancy
and not to go far away to the fields. They had also told her
that Merriweather had said that if the pregnant women chose
to have their babies far away at the lands, it was their own
affair, they should not call him to help them if they found
themselves in trouble. If they obeyed him and stayed in
Molepolole for their confinements then he and his staff would
do everything in their power to help. He often quoted the
proverb to them, 'He who disobeys his father's law will obey
the vulture's law'.

Mmapula blamed the harvest of that year; also her own
mother, the one who now spent much time with Dineo, was
with them at the lands and she had delivered Mmapula of her
children and other women also. All had been safely delivered
far away from the hospital at the lands. Why then all this fuss
about the younger women? When the new moon appeared,
the second night of it (which everyone could see and was
called 'the people's moon' in contrast to the first night when
it was only visible for a short time and then disappeared and
so was called 'the baboons' moon') Segametse said to her

mother, 'This moon is my ninth, I should go home now to be near the hospital. It is said that these days are different, a woman should give birth in hospital.'

'Yes, my child, I hear you, you speak well,' said Mmapula; but her eyes were gazing out at the field of whitening corn, a huge field, ripe for harvest, God's precious gift to a people accustomed to harvest failures. Every hand was needed, every minute of the short July days was crammed with work, women's work to go through the fields and cut off one by one the heads of millet and so gather in the harvest. Then there was the threshing. At least two months of hard work faced the women, and anyway her own confinements had given no trouble, except that Segametse's birth had taken a long time and she had bled profusely with Kabo. God had helped her: surely he would help Segametse and then the harvest would be gathered in? If they went home now to sit there all month waiting for labour pains to start, who would look after the harvest? What would they eat in the next twelve months? So the days went by; such busy days, full of hard work. The moon became full, shining like a beacon in the frosty winter sky. It began to wane; it rose late; it was seen in the early morning only.

Then Segametse spoke again. 'Take me home now, mother, I feel pains now and again and the baby is pressing into my pelvis.'

'All right, my child, you speak well,' replied Mmapula. 'We shall go home next week and you shall deliver at Merri-weather's place.' She thought to herself, 'By next week we shall have finished reaping; we can return to thresh later.'

That night the labour pains started. Segametse roused her mother and she and the old woman sat all night with the labouring child. She sat propped up against the mud wall of the small garden hut filled with acrid smoke from a small fire which the women kept burning all night. A smoky hurricane lantern gave a little dim light. The women warned Segametse not to make a sound: 'Women do not cry, only men do that,' said her mother; 'also if evil people hear cries they can bewitch us.' So when the pains gripped her Segametse made no sound, indeed one would hardly know that she was in labour.

The waters broke sooner than either of the older women had expected. 'I am surprised that she has paid the earth so quickly,' said the grandmother, 'the baby will come quickly now.' They sat on each side of Segametse massaging her abdomen and back fiercely, rubbing across her upper abdomen from side to side with a cloth. They massaged her back, her lower abdomen and her thighs, until in places the skin was excoriated. As the pains became stronger they massaged harder. They did not suggest that Segametse pass any urine and so her bladder rose higher and higher in her abdomen until it looked like a great balloon. Her underparts also swelled; sweat poured from her forehead. The pains continued with increasing intensity until dawn, and now Segametse groaned quietly, pathetically, with each contraction of the now tiring womb. She began to throw herself about in a panic for something told her that she would never deliver. The women scolded her and massaged until they too were weary. Then in the pale light of dawn Mmapula saw something and her heart leapt to her mouth for fear. A hand had appeared! The older woman saw it too, a small, cold, blue hand, swollen. She took it and pulled. The arm came out, like the hand, cold, swollen, blue, and then it stuck. No matter how hard and long the contractions were and no matter how hard Segametse pushed in horrified despair, the arm remained sticking out, unmoving, ugly.

'This is surely witchcraft,' moaned the grandmother. 'Ask Thuto to call the traditional doctor, Kalane, quickly.' 'Take me to Merriweather,' whispered Segametse in a tired, scarcely audible voice. But first Kalane came and threw his bones.

'The fault is the *dikgaba* of Thuto's sister,' pronounced the doctor. He meant that Thuto's sister had been upset at some time by Segametse or her mother and that was affecting the labour. The doctor made an infusion of herbs, and gave the bitter drink to Segametse. 'Now, if it is God's will she will deliver,' he said with unwonted optimism. The medicine made the womb contract fiercely so that it stood up pushing through the abdominal wall, but fortunately it did not rupture. The arm however did not move.

Mmapula was gripped by a great fear and a great remorse. Segametse's breathing was fast and shallow and she spoke little. The abdomen and thighs were greatly swollen and the lips dry and parched and the eyes rolling whilst the huge bladder swelling was frightening. Mmapula called Thuto. 'Rra Segametse,' she pleaded. 'Take your bicycle, go hard, tell Merriweather there is great trouble. Beg him to come or send someone to help.'

Thuto was young and strong and he pedalled hard as a man in a race—a race for his daughter's life. He took short cuts along narrow footpaths, through deep sandy dry river beds, over rocky places where he had to dismount and carry his bicycle. He reached the hospital when the sun was high in the northern sky; it was the time when working people break for lunch and when the shops are closed. When the doctor saw the agitation in Thuto's face and heard his urgent call, he broke his rule, as he had often done before, for who can leave a woman to die in labour? Not if one has seen it time and again. He called a driver and a midwife and they travelled as fast as the Land Rover would take them through the bush until, the sun hanging as a red ball in the low west winter sky, they reached the tiny hut. Dogs, hens and children scattered as the doctor with set face stooped through the low door into the semi-darkness within. Smoke from the wood fire smarted his eyes as he looked at Segametse, the swollen body, the cold blue arm sticking out, the pale sunken eyes; he felt the thready pulse, saw the shallow breathing and noted with accustomed horror the swollen bladder and loops of distended bowel under the abdominal wall. He knew he had arrived too late. He turned in anger to the two women, and blazed at Mmapula whom he knew well, 'You ignorant woman, you disobedient old woman, your disobedience has killed your child!'

'Forgive me, Merriweather,' whimpered Mmapula, 'Please

try, do your best, you have saved many women. God is great, he will help you.'

'Poor God,' thought the doctor, 'he gets blamed for everything.' The doctor turned to the nurse; 'We can do nothing here; this is an impacted shoulder with the baby long dead. We can only try to save the mother. Let's try to get a drip going and take her back to hospital.'

Segametse was placed on a mattress in the back of the Land Rover with midwife and female relatives with her. The driver took the vehicle swiftly yet skilfully over the atrocious roads. At 10p.m. Segametse was lifted tenderly into the labour ward. The doctor gazed once more at the bloated abdomen and tiny blue arm, now peeling, and put his stethoscope to the still chest. He turned to Mmapula, his anger now gone; only sorrow and despair filled his voice. 'She has gone, Mother,' he said, and turned away. Mmapula and her mother wept bitterly; the older woman threw herself on the ground and her shrieks rent the still silence of the night. After a little while she said, 'If God wills this, what can we do?' The doctor turned to say with renewed anger, 'Don't blame God for your disobedience,' but the midwife stopped him saying, 'Be patient, Doctor, our people will learn, but they learn only slowly and hardly.'

When Dineo was three months pregnant her husband said, 'I must go to the mines'. Before he left, Mmapula called him aside and spoke to him as a mother-in-law: 'God has considered your wife; she is not alone; she is indeed pregnant. I have already lost my firstborn. You must send money home so that she can be examined at the hospital and also she must deliver in hospital. The baby too, it will want clothes, soap and powder.' 'You speak well, Mother,' he replied, 'I want a child.' He was a good husband and each month Dineo went to the office of the Mine Recruiting Organization and collected her money.

Dineo attended the ante-natal clinic at the hospital. It was held twice a week: Wednesdays a woman went to register herself and have her first examination, and after that she attended on Fridays. Many women attended: lots of them were very young, unmarried girls; others were older with numerous babies. The clinic fascinated Dineo. Sometimes the clinic lasted well into the afternoon, but it was fun meeting all the other women and chatting away to them. A staff nurse would give a talk about what food one should eat when pregnant and how to wash babies, and she would tell those women with numerous babies that they could be sterilized and that other women could now space their babies and limit their families so that a woman need no longer have ten or more children whom she could not educate. There were student nurses who took blood samples, weighed the women, took blood pressures and examined them before giving them vitamin or iron pills. Dineo knew that the present rising moon was her third; she rather envied the educated women who used a calendar instead of the moon. Mmapula spoke often to Dineo telling her to listen carefully to all instructions given.

One night Dineo said, 'Mother, the pains have come'. Mmapula and her grandmother walked with her to the hospital. The night was pitch black and they were thankful for the soft light of their hurricane lanterns. It must have been around 1a.m. for the cocks were crowing for the second time: the old people said that the cocks crowed three times, at sunset, around 1a.m. and at sunrise. The hospital was brightly lit and Dineo was soon in the labour ward. A nurse, for some reason wearing a mask over her face, listened frequently to the baby's heart. The pains came strong and fierce and Dineo wanted to cry but an injection eased her pain. The night passed and the whole of the next morning, but Dineo's condition was good, so unlike her sister after a night of pushing before time and massage. When the sun was straight overhead the nurse said, 'Now you must push for your baby is coming'. Dineo pushed hard and then heard a baby's cry. The nurse said, 'Look, you have a baby boy'. Dineo thought it looked ugly—except the ears (which people always look at first) were nice, like her own. Three days later she was taken home in the hospital ambulance. Her mother ran out of the courtyard to welcome her, clucking like an old hen. She pulled Dineo's blanket hard over her head so that only her eyes were visible; no one should see a newly confined woman. She took her to the small hut at the back where her sleeping mat, blankets and pillow had been made ready; and so Dineo's three months of confinement began. The baby never left her side and each time he whimpered he was put to the breast, and so a close mother-child relationship developed and both were happy and contented. In a cardboard box by her side Dineo kept baby talc, soap, a face cloth and nappies. Mmapula laughingly said that when she was in confinement her mother had rubbed her and her baby with a red sand mixed with fat. Those days had gone now; only occasionally far out in a village was that custom preserved.

The second day home Mmapula took a razor blade and very deftly shaved the baby's head. Gathering all the hair together she burnt it so that not one piece was left for witches. Then she tied string round the baby's ankles and wrists. When these became tight they would know that the baby was growing well. Dineo was given large quantities of food—several times a day large basinfuls of soft sorghum porridge were taken in to her and often sour milk was mixed with the porridge. Dineo grew very plump and attractive. She rubbed her face daily with vaseline and her legs with glycerine and she noted with satisfaction her fattening thighs and buttocks. Her husband would indeed be pleased with her!

He returned from the mines when she had been two months in confinement and soon killed a goat for her, of which the whole family partook. He remained celibate, for custom did not allow him to sleep in his wife's hut and it was said that if he slept with another woman his child would become an imbecile.

At the end of three months Mmapula would bring Dineo and her baby out of confinement, and it would indeed be a special day with a tea party and prayers. Dineo's husband would kill another goat for the party and Thuto would announce the child's name, which was to be Morongwa, meaning 'messenger'. In the evening the Tswana doctor would come to unite Dineo with her husband according to custom. He would wash the husband's feet with water doctored with herbs, then they would enter Dineo's hut. The doctor would make a tiny incision in the skin near the umbilicus of both spouses, into which he would rub some medicine. Then he would burn some herbs which Dineo and her husband would inhale together under a blanket. It would now be safe for intercourse to take place and no harm would come to the child.

Mmapula did not find these customs inconsistent with her Christian faith and the minister and deacons knew that they were practised commonly, but of course they did not tell the white missionary as he would probably not understand. She knew that many people, especially the educated ones, were now neglecting these old customs. In order to make sure that Dineo did not become pregnant again before two years had passed, intercourse would only take place occasionally while she was breast feeding her baby, and she would feed him for at least two years because that also was said to prevent pregnancies. Dineo knew that this was hard on her husband and he was sure to console himself with other women, but if he did that secretly and looked after Dineo and the baby she would not ask questions. In any case Dineo had decided that when she came out of confinement she would discuss with her husband what Serwalo had told her, that a woman could take a pill once a day and that would prevent her falling pregnant. Her husband was reasonable and he might agree. Then he could visit her frequently and she would be happy. 'The snag is,' she thought to herself, 'men like an excuse for variety.'

In the meanwhile the October moon was only on the rise: there were still three weeks of rest, eating, fattening and then, when she did eventually emerge, she would be a real *motsetsi*, fat, healthy, a woman of whom people would say, 'She is lucky, her husband loves her and cares for her.'

5

SERWALO

It was just before 7.30a.m. when Serwalo walked with long steady strides through the stone gateway of the hospital. A large notice board announced to all and sundry that this was the Scottish Livingstone Hospital. Serwalo had already linked up with Hanna and Maria, two other enrolled nurses. All three looked fresh, smart and happy, white uniforms brilliant in the bright sunshine. Already a few out-patients were walking up the dirt road bordered by whitewashed stones, towards the out-patient department: women with babes on their backs, others leading bare-footed children by the hand. One woman, obviously very ill, was being pushed up the road in a wheel-barrow. On their left the nurses could see the engine house from which came a steady chug chug as one of the three generators supplied power to the hospital complex. Nearby the drivers, preparing their vehicles for the day's work, waved happily to the nurses. Mompati was already weeding the road edges, spade in hand, straw hat on his head, home-made cigarette hanging out of a corner of his mouth. He greeted the nurses respectfully and they in turn paused to ask him if he had risen well.

Serwalo skirted the path leading to the out-patient department, walked past the office block where Miss Shabane was already ushering her class of pupil nurses into the classroom for the first lecture of the day; she passed under the shade of the silver oaks and flowering jacaranda trees and entered the corridor leading to Matron's office.

There were already half a dozen nurses and domestic staff waiting to interview Matron Mrs. Margaret Motsepe, whose task it was to keep the wheels of this busy 180-bedded hospital running smoothly. Although an experienced administrator she had not been long at this hospital which, having been a mission hospital of the United Free Church of Scotland for 41 years, had recently been handed over to the Botswana Government. Mrs. Motsepe was an expert in handling her staff, using a mixture of sternness, sympathy, humour, cajoling, arguing, pleading and scolding! There were not many problems which she could not deal with. Her staff respected her; she was fair and just; not soft either. She demanded a high standard of nursing and a strict code of discipline. Serwalo stood outside the Matron's office and through the open window could hear faintly the various complaints and problems being dealt with.

Barati wanted her day off changed.

Masego's uncle had died and she needed two days off for the funeral.

Balebetse's child was reported very ill far away at the lands and she must drop all and go at once.

Neo and Thuso had quarrelled and each accused the other of cursing their parents.

Molly's husband had beaten her last night and would Matron please speak to him.

Sister Kgang said Nurse Mompati was cheeky and would not obey her.

Maria was ill and wanted to see the doctor.

Lerato had gone almost blind suddenly, after entering a new hut she had just built. Someone was jealous and had bewitched her and she must have a few days off to consult the traditional doctor.

Kgomotso said the vegetables were finished, whilst Molebatse reported that there was no food for the private patients.

Serwalo entered and respectfully greeted the Matron in setswana. Matron replied in English.

'Oh, Nurse Serwalo, they are short in the theatre today. I want you to report to Sister Lekoma straight after prayers and you will be in the theatre for a month.'

'Yes, Matron,' Serwalo dutifully replied. She was delighted as she loved the theatre—the green gowns and linen, the scrubbing up for operations, the smell of anaesthetics and antiseptics, the hiss of autoclaves, the packing of instruments in the sterile supply unit and above all the tense excitement of difficult operations. Monday was operating day and Mr. McArthur FRCS would be coming out from Gaborone for the majors. She hurried along to the hospital chapel where she joined the doctors and nursing staff for short prayers before the rush of the day began. Old Lebang, the hospital evangelist, conducted these in setswana. She liked the hymn with which they always opened as she and the nurses were excellent singers and harmonized well; but she was indifferent when he read from the Bible for his reading was poor, his spectacles held together by string. His prayer, too, was always the same. It was a bit better when Matron said to Dr. Merriweather, 'Will you please pray today, there are nurses taking examinations.' He would pray earnestly for them and for all who worked at the hospital and for the patients; of course his setswana tone was wrong in places but Serwalo could understand what he was trying to say and she was sure that God also would understand poorly spoken setswana!

Sister Lekoma said, 'Good, I'm glad you've come, we have a big list today. We must get moving.' She was very efficient; very conscious of the privilege that had been hers of studying theatre technique for a year in Edinburgh, Scotland. 'You would have to move faster than that in Edinburgh,' she would chide her nurses.

'Serwalo, you can scrub up for the three dilatations. Doug is doing them; he's a bit slow still, so you will be all right. I'll help the old man with the anaesthetics.' All this in setswana. Dr. Merriweather was already mixing syringefuls of pentothal, muttering behind his mask, 'I thought you would already have done this for me, Sister.' Doug Ramsay, a young Canadian doctor, a volunteer of the Canadian Universities Service Overseas Organization, was scrubbing up at one basin, Serwalo at the next.

The operation list nearly always commenced with a few *D* and *C*'s, the setswana translation being 'washing the womb', and it was a very useful and indeed popular operation—in the eyes of the patients a cure for all gynaecological and many other complaints as well.

The first case was Maria, an attractive young woman of some 20 years. Her strong white teeth smiled happily when the doctor jokingly said as he gave the pentothal, 'I see you have come for a baby!' He knew her well: married in church some eighteen months previously to David, a fine looking young man who had confidently expected her to become pregnant after a month of marriage; but the months slipped by and always on the rising moon Montle knew that she was not pregnant. David became very angry.

'You are doing this on purpose, you useless woman,' he scolded, 'I had better send you home and find a better wife, one who will give me a child quickly.' Maria said that she was ill and after four months of marriage he took her to the hospital where both of them were treated for the gonorrhoea with which he had infected her. Still the months went by and their misery increased. He struck her occasionally and there was no love in his love making. The traditional doctor said it was womb trouble, and at last David's parents said, 'Take her to the hospital and ask them to wash the womb.' The doctor agreed, for the marriage was breaking up and he had seen numerous women helped by this small procedure.

Doug found no abnormality, but the scrapings were sent away for examination. Three months later Sister Meswele saw Maria at the out-patient department and did a pregnancy test which confirmed Maria's hopes. David immediately went away to the Gold Mines of Johannesburg and each month sent an affectionate letter with a remittance to his happy wife.

The second case was different: Mosadimotho had an incomplete abortion and Doug swiftly cleaned out the pieces of retained tissue, and next day she went home with a packet of iron pills, where after three months she was re-united with her husband by the traditional doctor.

Julia had travelled well over 400 miles for her operation. She was a Mokalaka living in a tiny village north-west of Francistown. When the swelling in her lower abdomen became heavy and tiresome, her husband took her to the prophet Mokaleng, an elderly goat-bearded man who many years ago had founded his own church and whose village, far in the bush, was a Mecca for hundreds of sick and weary people. They came to him from all over Botswana, mental cases, sterile women and those with womb trouble. He would palpate their abdomens, lay hands on the sick, praying with great authority as a true prophet of God should and he would baptize them with a baptism that not only cleansed from sin but cured disease. All night long his white-robed followers would sing and dance, clapping their hands, praising and worshipping God. His fees were moderate, but a strong prayer and a special baptism would naturally cost money. After he had examined Julia he said to her husband, 'Take her to Merriweather in Bakwena country and ask him to remove this swelling which is the womb.' Julia introduced herself a few days later in Molepolole and an easy diagnosis was made of uterine fibroids. Doug and Serwalo both scrubbed up for this case to assist Mr. McArthur and Sister Lekoma, and Doug was amazed at the ease with which the surgeon removed the football sized tumour, while Serwalo learnt how to prepare sutures and hand instruments to the surgeon.

Just as they were closing the abdomen Serwalo saw the bearded face of the other Canadian volunteer peering round the door. Paul Kelly had been almost a year in Botswana. 'I've got a ruptured ectopic, she's desperate,' he cried. Serwalo thought that the patient was dead when she was brought into the theatre; she was deathly pale, breathing softly, rapidly, and her abdomen was swollen, full of blood. The anaesthetist called Serwalo to help him whilst the surgeon and sister opened the abdomen. She heard McArthur say, 'Soup ladle, please.' He ladled out several pints of blood which were filtered through gauze into a basin. The anaesthetist trans-fused the blood back into the patient's own veins, pumping hard to get the blood back in circulation. 'We call this auto-transfusion, using the patient's own blood,' he explained. Meanwhile the surgeon removed the ruptured tube which had caused the haemorrhage, and lying in the abdomen he found a tiny foetus just a few centimetres long. Serwalo was amazed at the team work which saved the woman's life; each one—surgeon, anaesthetist and sister—knew exactly what to do, and Serwalo longed to be like them.

The rest of the day's list went uneventfully—an old man with a hernia; an epileptic youth for skin graft to the burns he had received when falling in the fire in a fit; a child for removal of tonsils and a herd boy with a fractured elbow for plaster.

Serwalo liked the medical wards best of all because there was always such a variety of acutely ill cases, always something to challenge her nursing skills; always diagnostic problems. The ward rounds were interesting and sometimes fun, especially when Merriweather was in a teaching mood. He would stride into the ward and say to Serwalo if she happened to be in charge, 'Look at these beds, they're like a dog's hind leg, let's get them straight! And look at that locker, touching the wall and taking the paint off!' The smiling nurses would run and put everything straight, then the round would begin.

One day they stopped at Kgomotso's bed and Serwalo explained to the doctor that the patient had just come in from a far away cattle post with high fever and pain over the liver. When the doctor looked he saw that indeed there was a swelling over the liver and also numerous cut marks where the traditional doctor had tried his medications. The group of nurses that day was new to the wards and they were keenly and closely gathered round the patient, anxious to see and hear what the doctor thought.

'What do you see, Patricia?' asked the doctor of one of the new nurses. 'Oh, I see a swelling,' replied the nurse. 'And what else?' the doctor persisted.

Patricia looked rather embarrassed as she did not know if the doctor knew anything about the way traditional doctors worked. Eventually she said, 'I see cut marks where the Tswana doctor has treated her.' Kgomotso then explained that the Tswana doctor had sucked out four different poisons at four different places—human flesh, placental tissue, an insect and some dried leaves.

Serwalo, more used to the white doctor than the new nurses, now explained: 'This patient was poisoned by witch-craft, doctor; sometimes the poison is mixed with food, some-times it is slapped through the skin.'

'What about physiology, Nurse Serwalo?' the doctor asked her rather sternly, for she had passed well in anatomy and physiology. 'Surely anything introduced into the body will be digested and absorbed like any other food?'

Serwalo smiled patiently. 'These Setswana doctors are very clever,' she explained. 'They can do so much that we cannot understand. Anyway, I know what the diagnosis is in this case. It is an amoebic liver abscess and you will aspirate much pus from it.' The round continued; it was like going through a text book of medicine, and the nurses learned a great deal. There was Khumo, in and out with her asthmatic attacks, and this latest had nearly killed her. She was still on a drip through which powerful drugs had been given to dilate the constricted air passages. Serwalo was pleased with herself because she had started the drip herself to save the doctor's time. There was Mmakgosi who had arrived covered with boils due to a severe diabetes. Serwalo was now teaching her to inject herself with insulin. There were several cases of high blood pressure, very common in Botswana. There was old Sara with a stroke and so bad tempered. There were cases of rheumatic heart disease and enlarged hearts leading to heart failure. Bogadi had huge blisters in her mouth and was bleeding from her gums. She had *onyalai*, a type of purpura. There were cases of bronchitis, pneumonia, phlebitis, influenza, sinusitis, lumbago, conjunctivitis, dermatitis, and so on. Serwalo knew that there was only one disease that all the new doctors asked about because it was so common in their western civilizations. That was coronary thrombosis. They always asked why there were no cases of that killing disease and Merriweather always said, 'We do not know, but some cases are now being seen in Africans in large cities like Johannesburg.'

A few months in the medical wards and Serwalo had seen and nursed a great variety of cases. They came in and out all day long so that she and her nurses were kept running all day. She did not mind that—she was learning a lot and helping people.

The children's ward was similar. She once spent three months there. There were nearly forty cots and beds for both surgical and medical cases. She loved the children, so lovable and trusting they were. How they suffered! They were brought in with measles and its many complications; with broncho-pneumonia, gasping for breath; dehydrated with enteritis or dysentery. That was the great killer diarrhoea! There was often a delay in bringing the children for treatment. Many came with the fontanelle depressed and with signs of a witch doctor's poultice over it. Mpho had come in from the village of Ga-Thamagu, thin and dehydrated with chronic diarrhoea, and with long, rather dirty hair.

'I must cut the hair, mother,' Serwalo had said. 'No indeed,' replied the mother, 'that is beer hair and you must not touch it.' Serwalo knew that the Tswana doctor had treated the child for his diarrhoea and he had told the mother not to cut the hair until he gave permission, when he was certain that the child was better. He would then be paid by a large can of home brewed beer.

There were always cases of burns, especially in the winter months when toddlers would roll into the fire in the night or when epileptic children crouching round fires on cold winter nights would fall into the fire as their fits seized them. Serwalo loved to see the skin grafts which were done on these children. The commonest fracture amongst the children was that of the elbow, which was caused by small herd boys sitting on the rump of their galloping donkeys and being thrown off suddenly on to the out-stretched arm. What a difficult fracture it was to set, especially as it was usually a day or two before the child could reach hospital!

In the same block as the children's ward was the surgical. Serwalo regarded herself as a good surgical nurse, for she had spent some months under Sister Kgosiencho in this block, when Mr. McArthur would do his rounds very thoroughly, teaching the nurses just how he wanted his surgical cases cared for. Her patients were usually very good—very stoical, brave and trusting. One case she and all the staff remembered was old Modise who had one day presented himself at the clinic in Mmankgodi complaining of a large swelling in the lower abdomen. Serwalo had been most interested listening to the doctors trying to decide what this tumour could be. Such a tumour in a woman would give several possibilities, but in a man—well, the doctors were puzzled. 'I suppose it could be just a very enlarged prostate gland,' ventured Mr. McArthur as he scrubbed up and removed to everyone's delight what turned out to be a world record, as far as could be ascertained from medical journals, for size and weight of an enlarged prostate.

There was only one department of the hospital which Serwalo disliked, and even feared, and that was the TB block. There were always some sixty very ill patients, a dozen of them children. The Canadian Laboratory technician, Shirley, had one day shown her the tiny, red, rod-like bacilli under the microscope, which she explained to Serwalo were the cause of this dread disease. When Serwalo heard the patients coughing and when she had to dispose of their sputum mugs, filled each day with thick, yellow pus, she saw in her mind's eye millions of little red rods floating in the air. The wards were, however, light and airy and all the nurses had been protected against TB with BCG vaccination, so she knew in her heart that she feared unnecessarily!

The snag was, the patients only came when the disease was far advanced. Dr. Jacobsen used to show her the X-Rays. 'We never see such advanced disease in my country now,' she would explain to Serwalo. 'That is why treatment here is so difficult and prolonged.' Every day Serwalo and the other nurses would talk to the patients about this dread disease which was the biggest medical problem facing Botswana. They would explain how the disease was spread and how it could be cured, and that a person must not default from his treatment and that all members of the family should be brought for examination. Sesupo arrived one day just skin and bone, coughing blood continuously. Her husband had died of TB just a year before. With great difficulty Serwalo rounded up as many of Sesupo's close relatives as possible; three small children together with two nieces whom she had adopted and Sesupo's own mother. Two boys had recently left for the mines, but one had been sent home with a suspect lung. He was found at the cattle post far away with a letter, six months old, from the Mining Company, advising the Medical Officer at Molepolole that he had commenced treatment in Johannesburg and that the treatment ought to be continued. There were all kinds of TB cases in the wards, mostly lung infections, but also glandular cases, meningitis, hip joints, and spinal cases. Serwalo often felt saddened at the suffering this disease caused, but she took heart from the fact that the Botswana Government was making determined efforts to deal with the problem.

Serwalo's greatest thrill was the Kalahari safari conducted monthly from the hospital before the Norwegian Regional Medical Officer arrived to take over his work. They left early Friday morning, she and Elizabeth, a student nurse, together with Dr. Merriweather. The five-ton Bedford truck was carefully loaded and checked by old Station, who was now beginning to find driving in the Kalahari a bit of a strain. It was a young man's job. Drums of diesel and water were placed behind the cab, making excellent vantage points on which to sit when there was game around; boxes of medicines and food; blanket rolls; a small Honda electric generator; cooking pots, spade, axe, buckets, hose pipes for syphoning water and diesel out of the tanks; other tools; tyre patches, spare spring and fan belt, and so it went on. The doctor took his cook. There was the minister of U.C.C.S.A., a dozen or so patients and relatives, a few passengers begging lifts. There was hardly room to move, but Serwalo and Elizabeth nestled down amongst the bedding rolls and, pulling their blankets over their heads, went off to sleep—the best way they found of passing the weary hours of travel!

The trip took them some 200 miles west of Molepolole and lasted five days, the lorry grinding slowly through Kalahari sand with harder road surfaces here and there, where speeds of 30 miles an hour could be reached for a few miles. They stopped at all the Kalahari villages en route, villages with attractive names like Ditshegwani, Maboane, Takatokwane, Dutlwe, Motokwe and Tsetseng. At each village the lorry was unloaded and heavy boxes of medicines were carried into the local church or school or a hut borrowed for the occasion. The clinic was set up; patients were registered amidst excited shouting and clamouring; tea was brewed by the cook or a meal prepared of meat and rice. The work was arduous, especially in the heat of summer. Flies were everywhere, covering the food, the syringes, the medicines, and the bodies of the people.

Many of the people were unwashed and Serwalo found them rude and uncultured in the way they spoke and shouted, yet there was a loveliness about them and they came with great trust. All shouted for injections, ointment, drinking medicine and pills. The doctor always started the clinic with a Bible reading and prayer, and sometimes while the clinic was in progress the minister would gather the believers together and administer Holy Communion, or he would wait until the clinic was finished and then he and the doctor together would take the service. Serwalo found the singing in the village churches atrocious; the women had high raucous voices and often they sang out of tune, but they were happy in their faith and she could see as she sat in the little mud-walled buildings that they were sincere in their love for Christ and his gospel.

Serwalo's back nearly broke in some villages where there was no table and the bottles of medicine were placed on the floor; it was hard work filling the patients' bottles and putting ointment into the dirty tins they brought. Up and down she went, bending double.

At Salajwe there were many cases of malaria. Serwalo could spot them at once by their pallor, weakness and high fever. They told of many people who had died in the far away places. Between Salajwe and Takatokwane she had her first view of springbok: lovely, delicate antelopes leaping high across the track in front of the lorry. Station carried an ancient rifle and at one place halted the lorry, saying to the doctor with considerable optimism, 'I'll shoot one for our supper!' He stalked one beautiful male animal, flitting from bush to bush, but the bullet sailed far over its head, and so the team's supper leapt happily away, soon lost to sight in the far reaches of the eternal bush. The valley before Takatokwane was full of ripening corn, and there were herds of fat cattle watered at bore holes sunk 400 feet deep into the sand of the Kalahari, through dolomite, until the water-holding layers of limestone were reached. Herd boys galloped across the bush on wildly bucking horses that were only half broken in, and there were numerous scattered huts marking little farms.

Suddenly Serwalo saw two horsemen gallop out of the bushes and wave down the lorry. Station glared at them, for the next village was still an hour's drive away and the sun was already in the west.

'Come and help us, Merriweather,' pleaded the elder of the two as he dismounted. He was elderly, the skin of his face wrinkled deeply and his eyes bloodshot from years of living in the burning sunshine. He wore a jackal skin hat, a tattered khaki shirt and a pair of home-made skin trousers. His sandals were of eland skin.

'My daughter has been in labour for three days—it seems she cannot deliver; do please come.'

Station bush-crashed the lorry following the men for some two miles. He crashed over small shrubs and trees, winding his way between larger trees, dodging deep holes made by ant bears, roaring in bottom gear through deep sand. 'These Makgalagadi think the lorry is a horse,' grumbled Station as a thorn branch scratched his ear through the open window.

Eventually the horsemen stopped at a settlement of three small huts, surrounded by a solid fence of tree trunks. 'Come, nurses, let us see what we can do,' called the doctor. An elderly woman took the party round to the back of one of the huts;

naked little toddlers ran crying away as they saw the white man. A few goats scattered, together with the household dogs; flies were everywhere in their millions.

Gabanakgang sat on a goat skin mat, with her back against the wall of the hut, legs stretched out in front of her, obviously exhausted. She had been encouraged to push for two days, long before she should have. Doctor and nurses sat in the sand beside her, the nurses constantly waving the flies away while the doctor did his examination.

'I'll try forceps,' he said. 'I think there are twins.' Gabanakgang was laid gently on the floor. 'We shall give her chloroform; you will do that, Serwalo, and Elizabeth will help me. Perhaps you have seen me use chloroform before? It is an old Edinburgh habit.'

A few drops of chloroform on to some thicknesses of gauze and Gabanakgang was fast asleep. Swiftly the fly-covered forceps were applied and the first twin was delivered; the second soon followed, to the delighted clucks of the terrified women who were watching. One of the women quickly grabbed the placenta and buried it in the sand where neither hungry dog nor evil witch could find it. Another woman found a piece of old sacking with which she covered the babies as she nursed them.

'Give her penicillin and let us be on our way,' said the doctor. 'The sun is low and there will be crowds waiting for us at Takatokwane.'

'You have helped us greatly, you have saved three lives!' cried the elder of the two horsemen. But a year later Serwalo heard that the mother of the twins had died of malaria and the old women were struggling to feed the children on goats' milk and thin gruel.

Arriving at a village after sunset made the work doubly hard, especially if there was no moon to light up the scene. The people at Takatokwane had been waiting many hours and were hungry, tired and irritable! The Honda generator helped and soon the team was working in an untidy mud-walled classroom while Station put up the camp beds and the cook prepared a meal. At 10p.m. after the last patient had been seen, the team sat round the fire, appetites keen as they devoured platefuls of rice and meat. The fire was relaxing, conversation pleasant; stories were told, the Makgalagadi discussed. Before the camp beds were arranged round the fire for the night, the pastor prayed. He prayed earnestly for the journey, for the lorry, that it would not break down, as it was a serious matter to be stranded in the Kalahari. Then the men climbed wearily into their camp beds while the nurses and cook, in the privacy of a hut, stripped and washed thoroughly. 'Men are so dirty,' whispered Serwalo to Elizabeth. 'We never fail to wash, whereas they will only wash their hands until they reach home!'

The doctor liked to camp out in the bush, in wild places far from anywhere, so that he could have peace and also see wild animals; then Station would keep a big fire going all night, as lions, hyenas and jackals hated fire. Serwalo would put her bed on the back of the truck, safe from the lions!

The worst sand was between the villages of Motokwe and Tsetseng. At one point, over a slight rise, the lorry stuck in the sand, the back wheels spinning furiously. Everyone pushed hard after Station had packed branches underneath the wheels and slowly, inch by inch, the huge vehicle went forward. Sitting on the water tanks Serwalo saw lots of game—hartebeest, springbok, wildebeest, kudu, and once a horrible thing: a pack of wild dogs, wolflike in appearance, chasing a young eland with blood pouring from its side where the dogs had leapt upon it, tearing out the flesh.

It was at Tsetseng where Serwalo and Elizabeth saw their first really primitive Bush people, the Mosarwa of the Kalahari. She had occasionally seen them at home, but there they dressed like people and were civilized, specializing in sucking out disease. She had often heard people say, 'We'll call a Mosarwa doctor and he will suck out the poison for us.' But these ones here in Tsetseng in this isolated village were different. They sat at a distance from the Makgalagadi, in the shade of a camel thorn tree, waiting patiently until all the other patients had been seen; then they would come timidly forward, like shy, frightened little animals. Serwalo heard a Makgalagadi woman say, 'Now the dogs of the Kalahari can be treated.' The women had skin skirts, the men skin trousers and one carried his bow and poison-tipped arrows. Necklaces made of tiny round pieces of ostrich egg shell, and arm and leg bands similarly made, decorated them and around their necks each carried a tobacco pouch. Their faces were wrinkled, their eyes slanting, their ready smiles kind and gentle, their speech birdlike, full of clicks and other sounds which Serwalo delighted in but could not follow. Several of the children had syphilitic sores in their mouths.

One woman, a little older than the rest, had a huge fungous ulcer on her leg. 'Cancer,' said the doctor, 'due perhaps to constant abrasion by the bush and the fierce rays of the sun. We'll take her back if she will agree and cut it out and then skin graft the area. We may be in time to save her from a lingering death.' She did agree.

One small man had a huge soft swelling on the back of his neck and Serwalo was amazed when he agreed to go to hospital to have it removed. 'It is just a fatty tumour, easily removed,' explained the doctor.

At each village the church people gathered for services and to receive Communion. They sang happily, out of tune, with raucous voices. Gentle-looking church women dressed in their white blouses and black skirts reverently prepared the Communion table. Babies were baptized; new converts received, village pastors encouraged. It was hard work, non-stop hard work, travelling over rough roads, swaying and bumping with the bouncing vehicle until bodies ached, off-loading, setting up clinics, reloading heavy boxes, giving out medicines, hundreds of pills, injections by the score, setting up camp, breaking camp, having services, preaching, speaking about health, warning the TB patients to come every month—and all this with the noise of excited people and the intense Kalahari heat. Serwalo was glad when Tuesday came and the last village had been re-visited on the homeward journey. She ached all over, felt dirty and sand covered. At 10p.m. they reached the hospital, where the night nurses came running out with shouts of welcome and 'how many patients for admission?' Serwalo and Elizabeth sat together in a hot bath in the nurses' home telling their colleagues all about the expedition— the noisy patients, the delivery of the twins, the game, the hunters, the bushmen. So much to tell! The Kalahari was like a different world; one seemed to go back in time, to a time that seemed not to exist, a time that did not matter. Civilization was good, thought Serwalo as she relaxed in her bath.

'Thank goodness these trips will finish now,' she said. 'Thanks to the Norwegian government there will soon be clinics in every Kalahari village and Kabomo and his mobile team will take over until the clinics are staffed. I only hope I am not sent out there! Give me a town like Molepolole or Gaborone!

Serwalo knew that Peter was serious. His attitude was different from that of the other boyfriends she had, who just wanted to sleep with her and never mentioned marriage. She first met him at the community centre where the Scarers Band from Gaborone was having a dance. The centre was packed with young people and many of the boys had too much drink in them. Peter was quite sober and had his eyes on Serwalo from the moment she entered with other nurses. He noticed her bright face, her fine figure. He made his way towards her through the noisy crowd. He noticed her freshly plaited hair, nicely greased, and her brightly coloured slack suit. He danced with her several times and walked back to the hospital with her. He was a Molepolole boy, who had passed his O-levels a few years ago and was now working in one of the ministries in Gaborone.

The Scarers had electric guitars, the community centre its own generator; the noise was terrific, the band, the laughing dancers, the crowd of children's faces pressed to the windows. A few of the Swedish and USA volunteers were there.

Peter invited Serwalo to visit him in Gaborone on her next

day off. Serwalo loved Gaborone, it was so different from the rest of the country. She loved the Mall with its shops and supermarkets; she loved to see the tall government offices and the attractive parliament building with its arches and fountains. She loved the happy carefree atmosphere of the rapidly growing town: the streets were full of well dressed buxom girls and young men with gaudy shirts. Black and white mixed happily together. She loved the Holiday Inn, the cafés, the fruit and vegetable shops. If she was there on a Sunday she would go with Peter to Trinity Church, the Union Church, but it was mostly United Congregational people who attended, since the Methodists and Anglicans and others who formed the Union Church were now all building their own places of worship. Peter was a member of the church and that made her feel a bit ashamed, for it was usual for the boy to be outside the church and the girl to be a member. She determined in herself that if anything came of their friendship, she would become a church member. Then she and Peter would walk in the narrow path of faith together. One day Peter spoke seriously to Serwalo.

'I am now 29 years old and I have had my fill of running around. I love you and I want you to marry me.'

'Yes, I agree,' replied Serwalo. She knew that Peter had a good job with promotion ahead. 'But my parents are strict, they will not agree for us just to marry at the District Commissioner's office. They will want a church wedding.'

A week later Peter spoke to his parents: 'I am a man now; I want you to arrange a marriage for me. I have seen where I want to marry. She is a girl of Goora Tshosa ward, a nurse and well educated, the child of Thuto.'

'You speak well, my child,' replied his father. 'Indeed you are a man; we have sacrificed to educate you, and that family is a good one. We have no objection.' A few weeks passed by and then early one morning Peter's father and uncles went to see old man Thuto, telling him of Peter's desire to marry Serwalo. Thuto was cautious.

'I hear,' he answered. 'I have no objection; I will discuss the matter with my kinsmen.' He knew Peter's father well: a wealthy traditionalist like himself. There would be no problem with the bride-price. He called Serwalo who told him that she was quite agreeable to be married into Peter's family. Thuto's brothers and other relatives discussed the matter and all agreed that this would be a suitable match and that the two families would do well to be united in this way. They met with Peter's relatives and the bride-price was fixed at 10 oxen. It seemed to Serwalo that she and Peter hardly entered into the arrangements at all! One day Peter brought a blanket, a pair of shoes and a new dress to Thuto's home. He handed them to Mmapula: 'They are an engagement present for Serwalo,' he explained. Mmapula was glad, as this proved that Peter meant business; he really would marry Serwalo.

Three weeks before the wedding, one Saturday morning, Serwalo and Peter with their respective parents went to the weekly meeting of the church elders and deacons. 'We would like our banns called,' explained Peter's father. Rev. Mogwe entered the names in his book and said, 'Be sure, all of you, to come to church tomorrow to hear if I call the names correctly.' He knew, of course, that the old men would not come, neither would Serwalo. She would be too shy, but Peter and the women might come.

A day or two before the wedding Thuto with some men of his kgotla went early in the morning to Peter's father. They walked through the village in single file, and arriving at the kgotla sat on their home-made chairs, facing Peter's father and his male relatives who had been expecting them. No one spoke for a while, and then Thuto said, 'We have come for water.' After a silence Peter's father replied, 'Water is here; it will be sent to you.' Then Thuto and his men walked home in single file.

Early in the morning of the wedding day a long line of women walked in single file from Peter's place to Thuto's home. They entered the courtyard where Mmapula and the female relatives were waiting for them seated on their goat skin mats. There was complete silence for a few moments.

Presently Mmpula spoke: 'Good morning, in-laws,' she said. The women replied, 'Mmmm.' After a further silence Peter's senior aunt rose and said, 'Let us pray.' She prayed that God would bless all the arrangements for the wedding and that the marriage would be a fruitful one. Then she said, 'We are asking for water.' The wife of Serwalo's senior uncle then replied, 'Water is here; it will be sent to you.' The visitors then rose and walked home silently in single file. They reported their journey to their menfolk saying, 'We have brought the new wife home.' Thus did the two families and their immediate neighbours confirm the marriage. It was a real family matter, not just an arrangement between the two young folk. Custom was fulfilled, and now it would be the church's turn.

Just before 10a.m. Mr. Khan's lorry arrived at Mmapula's house where Serwalo and her bridesmaid were waiting. Serwalo looked very beautiful in her long white dress with a bouquet of artificial flowers; she was radiantly happy, although in the church and later at the wedding feast she would look very demure and even gloomy. Serwalo sat in the cab of the lorry while the others climbed on to the back. Her father of course did not go to the church, as he considered a church service just an addition to the important family agreement which had already been finalized.

Peter was waiting with his best man in the front of the church when Serwalo arrived. Smart he looked in his new black suit, white shirt and gloves. His best man carried a clothes brush with which every now and again he vigorously removed specks of dust from Peter's suit. Mmapula placed a springbok mat and a pillow before the young couple so that they could kneel in comfort. Rev. Mogwe exhorted the young couple, urging Peter to be a kind and considerate husband and Serwalo to be a dutiful and submissive wife. Deacon Galase prayed long and earnestly, particularly asking that soon the fruit of the womb would be in evidence. The bridesmaid had quite a struggle removing Serwalo's tight fitting glove so that Peter could place the ring on her finger. They sat together in the cab of the lorry as it took them back to Thuto's place, where for the rest of the day they sat in the courtyard under a canopy. The feast was more or less a free-for-all, with guests coming and going all afternoon. The matron and some nurses arrived around 4p.m. and were given special seats in the hut reserved for important guests. Food was plentiful and well prepared—huge platefuls of meat with rice, potatoes, beetroot, carrots and so on were handed round by numerous willing helpers, and these were followed by tea and cakes. At the back of the courtyard large pots of beer were brewing and Thuto's witch doctor was also to be seen, although the deacons turned a blind eye to these things. In the courtyard near the bridal table sat church women singing hymn after hymn, whilst outside the courtyard girls and youths were singing and dancing. The noise could be heard far and wide. All was happiness. Towards sunset the presents were shown by the best man who held each gift up for all to see.

'Here is a bucket from Neo so that Serwalo can fetch water each morning. Here is a teapot from Magdalene in which Serwalo will make her husband's tea. Here is a mat on which Serwalo will sit as she talks to Peter. Here is a wash basin from the nurses, in which she will pour hot water so that her husband can wash each morning. Here is a three-legged pot in which she will cook his porridge.'

Later in the evening deaconess Masego closed the long day with prayer; it had indeed been a day of prayer, hymn singing, dancing and laughter. Tomorrow there would be another day of feasting. Then there would be a feast at Peter's place and after a few days Mmapula would take Serwalo to her mother-in-law.

Both she and Peter had only a few days leave. Serwalo returned to her nursing duties and Peter to Gaborone. They met at weekends or whenever Serwalo had a day off and was able to rush in to Gaborone. She never knew when she would be transferred. Most educated married couples worked and were often separated by many miles. Married life was not easy.

After six months Serwalo reported to Matron that soon she would need maternity leave.

6

MOSETSANAGAPE

W HEN SHE WAS BORN all agreed that they were disappointed that a male child had not arrived. They also agreed that she should be called *Mosetsanagape*, meaning 'another girl'. Thuto and Mmapula watched her as she strode away to school, case on her head, carriage erect, long smooth strides, and they were proud of her. Their early disappointment had long since gone, and Mmapula felt that Mosetsanagape was the best of her children, one in whom she took great delight. She was always polite, rather reserved, quite clever and very religious, more religious than all her other children, and her faith seemed to transform her whole life. It was different from her mother's quiet, orderly faith; there was more spontaneous joy to it, more dancing and singing and clapping of hands.

Mosetsanagape was in her third year at Chief Kgari Sechele school, the only secondary school in Molepolole. This was an important year for her, for she was to sit the Junior Certificate Examinations in a month's time. Ted Stephens, the headmaster, and some of his staff used to say that it was time that that examination was done away with and that they should just concentrate on the Cambridge O-levels examination taken two years after the Junior Certificate. But the J.C. examination was useful for sorting out the students, since those who failed it could not go on and try for their O-levels. This meant that every year several thousand young people left school with three years' secondary education but no certificate, and they wandered around the country looking for jobs. Mosetsanagape knew that if she had that J.C. doors would open to her for further studies, for typing and enrolled nursing and teacher training. It was worth having, but she was aiming higher than that; she wanted a university education, a B.Sc. degree, and if she did well she knew that the

Government would give her an opportunity to study medicine in Zambia, Nigeria, Uganda or Kenya. She was in earnest; she meant to get on.

She stepped out briskly in the early morning sunshine, soon joined by other teenagers going to the same school. She crossed the 'camp', a relic of British rule, that area where the central Government had its offices—the District Commissioner, the revenue officer, the police, veterinary, agricultural, and post offices. Station Commander Bogatsu was already drilling his platoon of smart policemen. The District Commissioner with his assistant and his clerks and typists would arrive a little later. There were numerous government houses in the 'camp', some small, type 5, some larger types 1 and 2, and many more small houses were being built. Senior civil servants lived in the type-2 houses, but the rent was rather high and if one wished to save the rent allowance paid monthly by the government one could find a small house to rent privately in the village; then the rent allowance could be used to buy cattle, or it could be saved. Molepolole was just like every other town and village in Botswana, houses of brick and corrugated iron roofs going up fast. Thuto said he had never seen so many white people in Molepolole in all his life. Before independence there were just a few, and everyone knew them, the Afrikaans traders, the District Commissioner, the veterinary and agricultural officers, the police officer, the doctors at the mission hospital. Now the whites were numerous, mostly known as 'volunteers' who had come from many different countries to do some special job for a couple of years. Mosetsanagape saw many of them every day. They came from Britain, the USA, Norway, Sweden, Denmark, West Germany and Canada. They all spoke English, but some of them knew only a little of that language, and spoke with strange accents. To Mosetsanagape they all looked the same—the girls fair with long hair and flat buttocks, wearing jeans; the boys with beards and long untidy hair, dressed in bright shirts and denim jeans. Mosetsanagape always wondered why they did not dress properly! Was it that they dressed like that in their own countries or that they thought they could dress as they liked in Africa? People wondered why they did not wear jackets and ties; to wear a jacket was a sign of respect, one would never go to visit the chief without a jacket! And certainly no one would go to church without a jacket! Yet these young volunteers did not worry about these things, and even the few who attended church did not wear jackets, just going casually along in their shirt sleeves.

Mosetsanagape came to realize that this was one of the changes of the modern world, a rebellion against old ideas and orthodoxy, and she knew that many of the students at school and at university in Gaborone were copying the ideas, the freedom of dress, the life and speech of the young volunteers from Europe. She could see also that in spite of their casual dress and strange ways, many of the volunteers were doing a good job of work, helping the country to progress. Some were well qualified, trained teachers with degrees, doctors, radiographers, laboratory technicians, dentists, engineers, accountants, pharmacists and so on. A few had come just to have a good time, drinking a lot and sleeping with the local girls, but most were serious. Students said that they were the new missionaries, the new colonists, but they had little power and no political rights and they did not stay for more than a year or two. Also they only came on the invitation of the Botswana government. Some of the senior students at school used to say, 'These are the modern missionaries but they do not trouble us with Bible rubbish and tell us not to do this or that. They drink with us, eat in our cafés, hitch-hike around our country, live in our huts and marry our girls.'

Mosetsanagape had herself heard some of the volunteer teachers talking about religion. They said that God was a myth, a myth exploded by science, and that the young people of the west believed in atheistic humanism and scientific agnosticism. Many of the boys loved this type of talk and believed it all. It was modern, it gave freedom, permissiveness. 'This is our new life of independence, we can do what we like,' they used to boast, as they drank their beer at

Mokone's café. Mosetsanagape was glad that there nearly always seemed to be other expatriate teachers who spoke differently, who confessed to be Christians and who encouraged the students to talk about religion and to attend the weekly meeting of the Student Christian Movement.

The boarders had finished their breakfast when Mosetsanagape reached the school gates, the assembly bell already ringing. Over 700 young people were packed into the dining room-cum-hall. The assembly was taken by Bob Boxley from the USA, who began to read from the book of Proverbs, much to the disgust of a group of boys who growled their disapproval. Then the day's work began, just as in any other secondary school.

The school, built with a grant in aid from Britain, was quite well equipped, with science laboratories, classrooms, dormitories and a fine library gifted by the British Council. Pressure was now on, as next month would see the J.C. and O-level examinations. Mosetsanagape was not the only one who realized that education could open many doors to a new and interesting life. She plodded hard and her teachers encouraged her. Some of the expatriate teachers became discouraged, complaining that many of the students played the days away thinking that they could pass their examinations easily without hard work. 'It is true,' said Mosetsanagape to the boys who plagued her for sex every day. 'How can we pass our examinations if we just play around?'

On Wednesday afternoons Mosetsanagape, together with some sixty other students, attended the weekly meeting of the Student Christian Movement. She enjoyed this immensely, as did all who attended. They conducted the meeting themselves, in English. It was good practice to speak English in public and it was fun trying out one's knowledge of idiomatic English. Sometimes an interested teacher would come along and encourage the students. Sometimes outside speakers would attend. Three years ago quite a few of the young people, including Mosetsanagape, had come through a religious experience of conversion. A young man, Nat Kgosi, had come from Johannesburg with a group of young folk. They stayed for a week at the school, holding meetings and discussions every day. They brought a new look religion: they were Africans, black, like Mosetsanagape, they spoke Zulu, Setswana and English. They made the Christian faith live, with their simple, vital, relevant, happy message. They said that Christ was real, not just a missionary's fairy! He was for blacks! He could save Africa and set men free! He was for young people! He could change hearts and he could show people how to live a good, pure and exciting life. The students crowded round Nat each day, asking questions, discussing religion. Nat and his team taught them new songs; they sang with clapping hands, dancing feet, harmonizing; there was joy in the heart, eyes were bright and faces laughing.

'There is a big wheel turning in my heart . . .'

'You can't get over it . . . under it . . . round it . . . the love of God.'

'Christ can save Africa . . . Molepolole . . . our secondary school . . . all of us.'

At the end of a week Mosetsanagape gave herself unreservedly to Jesus Christ. She told her mother who was delighted, but her father merely said, 'If it makes you more obedient I'll be satisfied.' She told her classmates, some of whom laughed, saying she would miss the fun of life. Every week the group met together to share their new found, happy, uninhibited faith. They addressed each other as 'sister' or 'brother' and whenever one spoke in the meeting he would begin with, 'I greet you all in the name of Jesus.' They discussed all kinds of topics—the inspiration of the Bible; the value of prayer; race; politics; witchcraft; sex. At one meeting they decided that for them sexual relations, which were the normal pattern of behaviour in the school, were out. Indeed at the close of the discussion the chairlady, Sister Margaret, asked all who had been having such relationships and who would now cease to hold up their hands. The response was good.

Mosetsanagape had a new urge, a new aim in life now. She wanted to be a Christian, a real one, whose light would shine into the world. She gave herself wholeheartedly to her studies; she wanted education, a university degree; then later marriage, a family and a job. She wanted to make Botswana a Christian country. She had known the Christian faith from her early days, for her mother had taught her Bible stories and prayed frequently with the whole family. She had attended Sunday school and church. She had been taught Christian morality from her earliest days. Her mother was strict about such things, and when she was thirteen had warned Mosetsanagape frequently about the danger of pregnancy. She had only once been thrashed by her mother, and that was when she was caught returning home early one morning. She was not asked where she had been. Her mother knew what had happened and she made her hold the centre pole of the hut whilst she beat her with the supple *maretlwa* stick used for disobedient children. Her mother watched anxiously for the next rising moon, but Mosetsanagape was lucky. Mmapula knew the constant anxiety of mothers with teenage daughters, who had sacrificed to send their children to school and then all was wasted through a pregnancy. Since her religious experience Mosetsanagape easily resisted the advances made by the boys in her class, merely saying, 'I'm not interested now.' And the boys were furious, for she was most attractive.

Soon after her conversion Mosetsanagape and the whole group went to inform the minister of the local United Congregational Church of their desire to follow Christ and to become church members. Rev. Mogwe was delighted. He called them one Saturday morning to the deacons' court where each in turn told of how God had spoken to them and of their surrender to Jesus. The old deacons, mostly un-educated but godly men and women, listened enraptured and thrilled. They counselled the youngsters, telling them of the difficulties of the straight and narrow way, of the snares of the devil, of the pitfalls and the permissiveness of the age. On the following day at morning worship each of them was called to stand while their names were read out, so that the whole church knew of the new converts. They were told to attend the doctor's Bible class every Sunday morning for instruction in the faith and that soon they would be received into the church. Mosetsanagape loved the Bible class, held each Sunday morning. Over a hundred secondary school students attended; they conducted the meeting themselves—one was chairman, one prayed, some conducted the singing of choruses and hymns; there were Bible quizzes and discussions and the doctor or one of his colleagues gave a short talk from the Bible applying its teaching to everyday living.

One day Merriweather said, 'I want eight of the Bible class to come with me to Letlhakeng next weekend. We shall have a youth meeting on Saturday night and Sunday services, and we shall try to make some new converts.' Mosetsanagape's heart leapt in hope. O that she could be chosen! She would go willingly; she had never seen Letlhakeng and she had a message burning in her heart which she would love to pass on to the Makgalagadi young people.

She was chosen along with three other girls and four boys. Straightaway she began to rehearse in her mind what she would say in her first public speech! On Friday afternoon the girls bought flour, sugar, salt and tea. They baked scones and 'fat cakes'. The party left early in the afternoon of the next day, a hot summer's day. They climbed on to the back of the Chev' truck and in spite of the burning heat of summer sang at the tops of their voices all the sixty kilometres to Letlhakeng. The bush looked fresh and green after the rain showers of early summer, and brightly coloured desert flowers gave vivid colouring amongst the green. At one spot a puff adder slid across the road, narrowly escaping death, and the singing ceased for a moment whilst everyone shouted, *noga!*, snake!

In the late afternoon they entered Letlhakeng, the first and largest settlement of Makgalagadi people west of Molepolole. Mosetsanagape was quite amazed at the size of the village spread out over low hillsides with a broad valley between. She saw numerous mud huts, not so nicely thatched as those in Molepolole, but what amazed her was the number of brick and corrugated iron buildings spread through the village—

trading stores, a bottle store, offices, a clinic, police station, schools and teachers' houses! 'My word, the Makgalagadi are advancing now,' she remarked to her friend Nelly. 'They are just like us now; they are educated, dress properly and can vote in elections.' Both she and Nelly were Bakwena, aware that their fathers still regarded the Makgalagadi as servants, as inferior people.

The truck stopped at the pastor's house just next to the attractive, blue-roofed church. There were three dwelling houses in his courtyard, the largest a three-roomed oblong hut with an iron roof; the others round huts nicely thatched. Rev. Diphoko was proud of the way he kept his house and church. The larger of the thatched huts had been placed at the disposal of the team, where they all—boys and girls—slept in a circle on the cool mud floor. The doctor shared the oblong hut with the pastor and his wife and a few grandchildren. A group of church women were stamping corn for the evening meal, and Mosetsanagape and the other girls soon joined them. After sunset plates of sorghum porridge, *bogobe*, were given to the visitors, and at 8 p.m. they went over to the church where a crowd of people had already gathered. Hurricane lanterns lit up the building and through the dull flickering light the team could see the shadowy faces of an expectant people. Rev. Diphoko introduced the doctor and his team. Each team member then introduced himself. There were gasps of amazement when Koagile said, 'I am Koagile of Molepolole, and I am studying Form 5 and I hope to become a doctor.' Such educated young people had never been seen in Letlhakeng church before, where a secondary school was still a thing of the future. The meeting went on until around midnight. The team sang their lively choruses:

The things I used to do, I do them now no more,
The things I used to say, I say them now no more,
The things I used to think, I think them now no more.

They did sketches, some gave short addresses, while a few

(including Mosetsanagape) were asked to tell of their own faith and how Christ saved them. When she rose to speak Mosetsanagape felt her knees shaking and her mouth went dry, but in simple words, eyes aglow, face radiant, she told how she had given herself to Jesus Christ. 'Now I have Jesus in my heart,' she said as she sat down. At midnight Koagile, the Chairman, invited all who would like to give themselves to Jesus to come forward—to which invitation thirty-six people, mostly young, responded.

One middle-aged woman was weeping and moaning with occasional loud shrieks. 'That is the Spirit of God wrestling with her stubborn heart,' cried the pastor jubilantly. 'I've been waiting for her for years to return to Christ.'

Next day the team travelled twenty miles further west to another small Kalahari village where a happy service was held in a school classroom. The headman's wife came forward saying, 'God has spoken to my heart; I will now repent and believe.' Elderly church women danced round the truck as the singing team climbed aboard for the journey home. All the way home song after song, hymn after hymn was sung by the happy team. Night descended, and with the night the stars; Venus hung in the west like a bright lantern, the Milky Way was clear with a large hole in the middle, the Southern Cross lay on its side. It seemed as though a million stars and all the host of heaven danced and sang with the team that night!

'There is joy in heaven tonight,' cried Patiko as he gazed upwards. 'Beyond those stars the angels are writing new names in the Book of Life!'

Only as the truck entered Molepolole did the team fall into silence. Mosetsanagape and a few others alighted in the town, waving farewell to the boarders. 'See you tomorrow,' they shouted one to the other. 'Don't forget we have a geography test.'

Mosetsanagape joyfully told her mother of the day's activities and in her heart Mmapula gave thanks for a good daughter whom she could now trust. 'She'll get married, I am sure,' she thought to herself. 'She will not just have babies outside of marriage.' Mosetsanagape slept, weary and tired, with a great peace in her heart. 'Thank you God, you have used me today.' Her whole being thrilled at that thought!

Mosetsanagape's greatest excitement was when the doctor invited the team to travel with him to Serowe, the capital of the Bangwato people and the hereditary home of Sir Seretse Khama. She had never of course been to Serowe, some 250 miles away, and she knew it was the largest village in Botswana and very progressive, with lots of shops, community halls and modern homes. The Bangwato were rich, many of them having huge herds of cattle. The team reached Serowe one hot Saturday afternoon in time for a rally of young people. The great UCCSA church was well filled with students from the teacher training school, Swaneng secondary school and other schools. The team members were in good form and this time Mosetsanagape spoke with more courage, and she saw from the way the congregation looked intently at her that her message was going home. Koagile and Patiko wrote down the names of about eighty people who responded to the call. On Sunday morning the church was packed—about a thousand people had come. The team were at the top of their form, singing, preaching, testifying with great sincerity. The doctor preached and there was a great hush over the vast congregation. At the close of the service the team wrote down 200 names of people who confessed Christ. Never had they seen so many converts at one time and they could hardly believe their eyes!

The multiplicity of churches troubled Mosetsanagape not a little. Thuto often told her that in Chief Kgari's day there were only two churches in Molepolole that the chief recognized, the LMS and the Anglican. Dr. Livingstone brought the LMS church to the Bakwena when he arrived in Kolobeng in 1846. It was said that he made only one convert, the Chief Sechele, but Mosetsanagape used to say to the other students (some of whom ridiculed Livingstone's work): 'If he converted the chief, he would win the tribe, and we are here today because of Livingstone's work.'

She had learnt quite a lot about the early missionaries in the Bible class. Livingstone was followed by missionaries of the German Lutheran Church. One day the Bible class had an outing to Dithejwane where the Bakwena used to live in a rocky fortress for fear of the Boers, and there she saw the memorial stone to several German missionaries who had died of malaria. After five years or so Sechele called his first missionary society back again and so the LMS sent out dedicated men who spent their whole life in Africa; men like Robert Moffat, father-in-law of Livingstone, who translated the Bible into setswana and who wrote numerous hymns in setswana; Roger Price, sometimes called the Great Lion of Bechuanaland; MacKenzie who became a Resident Commissioner and Willoughby who went to London with the three chiefs. These men made many converts, and organized the church in Botswana; nearly all the chiefs became Christians and the LMS, which was the mission of the nonconformist churches in Britain, became as it were the state church of Botswana. The Anglican Church came much later, and Kgari used to say when other churches wanted to come into his territory, 'No, I have two churches and that is enough.'

It was after independence in 1966 that other churches began to multiply, because the new government said that there should be freedom of religion and each person could worship in his own church. The so-called indigenous churches soon multiplied and Mosetsanagape sometimes wondered if she was missing anything by not joining them. The first to appear was old Keikanetswe's 'Church of God'. Soon, however, some of his members broke away and started their own churches. Each leader claimed that he was a prophet sent by God with healing powers. Each new sect was given its own name, 'Church of God in Christ', 'Spiritual Healing Church', 'St. John's Healing Church'. Mosetsanagape was told that there were over twenty of these sects in Molepolole. Thuto used to become quite heated when he talked to his family about them. 'These so-called prophets are just here to make money out of the ignorant,' he would angrily declare. 'They have never been to college or school. Ask them to show us their certificates!' Nevertheless these prophet sects seemed to give the people something they missed in the orthodox churches. Each leader was charismatic, had personality and drive. They prayed, shouting to God, dressed in their robes of white, or red, or blue. Lifting their hands up to heaven they looked like ancient prophets calling down God's blessing upon their land and its President; calling for rain and seeking power for healing the sick. Then they laid hands on the sick; they tied coloured cords round the waists of their followers; they baptized their converts in the muddy pools of the Molepolole river. At night they would sing, dancing round and round in a circle, stamping the ground until it vibrated, the prophet and his people together hour after hour in ecstasy. As they stamped and clapped they chanted, the men with deep bass voices, singing over and over again, 'We are tramping on Satan: we have found a Saviour.'

Such singing would touch the hearts of the people so that soon all who were near would be joining in crushing Satan with their pounding feet and often a woman would fall to the ground shrieking, beating her breast in agony as the spirits of Satan and Jesus fought for her soul. Then in the morning the prophet would call for a beast to be slaughtered, and he with his followers would feast together eating vast quantities of meat. So the prophet became rich, for his people fed him, the women stamping his corn and giving him gifts of goats, corn, mealies and beans, as God prospered them.

It was always at the Independence Day celebrations that Mosetsanagape saw these churches best. There was always a united churches service at the stadium. The churches of Molepolole came, each vying with the other in dress, in numbers and in singing! They came with banners flying— the UCCSA with their white and blue banner with a dove of peace; the sects with their prophets at the head, arriving late so that all could see them, in long lines, chanting. Some of their leaders wore clerical collars, some were bishops.

There would be prayers and a sermon, each church leader taking it in turn with each new year of independence to give the sermon. Then after the Blessing which was often given by the Roman Catholic priest, who because his congregation was relatively small in Molepolole could not be given the sermon to preach (and in any case he *liked* to give the Blessing), the whole congregation would stand and sing the national anthem.

The choirs would lead, the people would sing with uplifted faces, the beautiful words of the national hymn would be carried in gracious harmony into the clear hot sky:

1. This is our land
   A gift from God
   Our heritage, left by our fathers
   May it be at peace.

   Chorus:
   Awake, awake men, awake
   Stand up, women, stand up, determined
   United to serve our land!

2. Beautiful and famous name
   That of Botswana's nation!
   Through our unity and our peace
   It is united as one nation.

Thuto would say when he heard about the service afterwards, 'The Government should stop this nonsense!' Mmapula would cry, 'They are stealing our members!' In the secondary school the students discussed the sects and their prophet leaders, some saying, 'They are good; there are no whites leading them; this is African religion, this is black theology.' Others said, 'They are good, because they have a healing ministry and they catch the spirit of Africa.' Mosetsanagape and her friends said, 'They may be good, but for the time being we will stay in the church of our fathers, for we have already found Jesus there.'

The annual meetings were held in the second weekend in October. The whole family was delighted that Mosetsanagape was to be baptized and received into full membership of the church. Thuto had a feeling of pride; the same pride that he experienced when his children passed their examinations or when Serwalo passed her final nursing examination. He would not go to the church, of course, but he would give any money needed for Mosetsanagape's confirmation dress and for her church membership ticket.

People began to arrive from the outside villages on the Thursday evening, travelling in lorries hired for the purpose. The people from Ga-Thamaga always came to Thuto's place for sleeping; they filled his three huts and sometimes they slept outside if they were many. Each pastor brought a group of church people and those to be confirmed. The people of Tsetseng and Motokwe had travelled two hundred miles across the Kalahari in order to be present. All came eagerly, hopefully, praying that God would bless them and their work for him and that they would have happy hours chatting with old friends again.

Mosetsanagape was unable to attend the business meeting on the Friday, but in the evening she heard her mother talking to Thuto about the discussions. Finance was a problem, many members were behind in their givings and collections, especially in the village churches. 'If you want ministers you must look after them and pay them,' Merriweather had chided. 'All the young educated men go to government service because we pay so little to our ministers,' warned Rev. Mogwe.

There was a discussion about the young people and how to win them to the faith, and how to keep them in the church.

'They come in at one door and within a few months they leave us by the other door.'

'We loose them through pregnancies outside of marriage, and strong drink pulls others away.'

'It is because they have money and status that they don't need God.'

'The educated laugh at us, the civil servants, the nurses, the teachers, because they are better educated than we are.'

So moaned the village pastors, sincere men, but on the whole men who were conscious that they were not well educated.

Saturday was a busy day for Mosetsanagape, a day of great excitement! She arrived at the church around 9a.m. for her interview with the ministers and deacons and found about a hundred others who had been called for interview. When she was called into the church she sat nervously facing the assembled dignitaries. She was asked questions: 'When were you converted?' 'Are your parents Christians and have you been baptized?' She answered well, and the minister said, 'Be back at 2 p.m. for the baptism service.'

Mmapula had made an excellent job of Mosetsanagape's baptismal dress, and she looked really beautiful with her white dress, white beret and white shoes, as she sat with the others in church. Her face shone, large eyes bright with expectation, her skin clear, smooth and shining with the lotion she had applied. Her heart thumped with excitement; she was to be baptized as one of Christ's believers!

She stood with a hundred others as the minister asked the questions.

'Do you believe that the Lord Jesus Christ is your Saviour and Lord?'

'Do you want forgiveness of sins?'

'Will you from this day renounce all evil and faithfully follow Christ?'

To each question Mosetsanagape gave a definite yes.

Each candidate then came forward in turn and knelt before the minister. When her turn came, Mosetsanagape was nervous, sweating much in the heat and excitement. The minister pushed her beret back a little. She looked up into the kind, fatherly face as he dipped his finger in water and made the sign of the cross on her forehead. The water trickled down her nose and onto her dress and she heard, as it were from a far distance, the great words, 'Mosetsanagape, I baptize you in the name of the Father and of the Son and of the Holy Spirit.' A great peace flooded her soul such as she had never experienced before. If only her father had been there to share the experience!

Sunday was hot, boiling hot, as October should be before the rains. The huge church was packed out; the people to be received sat in the front seats, their white dresses resplendent in the afternoon sun which poured on them through the west windows. Mosetsanagape sat with others from the secondary school who were to be received. She looked around and saw that most were young people like herself, with here and there an elderly woman. There were few men, for the church in Botswana was a woman's church—not that the men were antagonistic, they just could not be bothered. The minister preached earnestly from the verse, 'You are the light of the world.' He urged the new members to be lights shining for Jesus in the darkness of the world around. After the sermon the new members were received into the church by being given the 'right hand of fellowship'. Mosetsanagape's hand was wet and her neck arteries pulsated as she heard the words, 'Mosetsanagape, we receive you into Christ's church, and as a sign we take your hand. May the Lord bless and keep you.'

The service took a long time, for it included Holy Communion. There was a great hush in the church as deacons took round the bread and the wine. The reverent silence was broken only by the sound of babies gurgling at the breast and the bleat of an inquisitive goat at the far door. Because it was so hot people sweated; some fanned themselves; flies buzzed around seeking the bread and wine.

When the deacon reached her, Mosetsanagape was given a tiny glass cup full of red wine and covered by a little aluminium lid on which was a piece of bread. When each one in that vast congregation had received this cup, with the deacons and ministers, the presiding minister said, 'Let us eat this bread remembering our Lord Jesus Christ whose body was broken for us.' Seven hundred hands took the bread and all ate together, and because the bread had been dried hard by the heat there was a crunching noise heard all over the church as they ate.

Then Mosetsanagape heard the words again spoken by the minister, 'Let us drink this cup remembering our Lord Jesus whose blood was shed for us.' Seven hundred heads were thrown back as seven hundred cups were drained so that no drop was left. Mosetsanagape's heart was happy and at peace. She thought to herself, 'Now I am one of Christ's believers and I have eaten his flesh and drunk his blood. These will strengthen me in my resolve to follow him to the end.'

That evening at home there was a tea party. That was custom. Fat cookies had been prepared by Mmapula and scones baked over the fire. There was meat and rice also. A dozen or so friends gathered in Mmapula's courtyard, the women sitting with legs straight out on goat skin mats, the men on chairs. Mosetsanagape, still in her white dress, sat in the centre, radiantly happy. Hymns were sung, deacon Totolo read from the Scriptures and offered prayer that Mosetsanagape would walk in the straight and narrow way and not be drawn away by love of the world.

That night Mosetsanagape put her white dress away in a suitcase which stood on four little stones to prevent white ants from reaching it, and as she slept she felt that her heart was as clean and white as the dress.

Monday brought her back to earth. Examinations were near, teachers becoming irritable; work piling up; Mosetsanagape thought she would never finish the work. She studied hard, returning to the lights of school every evening for study. She prayed daily and fully believed that the God whom she served would not fail her and that he would see her through her exams. In due time he did.

One night she spoke gently to her sister Serwalo who was slipping out to meet her boyfriend and tried to warn her of the danger. Serwalo retorted angrily, 'I am your elder sister, do not talk to me like that!' She banged the door so noisily that she nearly wakened her mother. Mosetsanagape just continued to pray for her. And it was then that Peter came into Serwalo's life.

7

KABO

KABO REALLY ENJOYED SCHOOL even though he was only in standard 2. There were some forty children in his class and around eight hundred in the Canon Gordon primary school. The school was crowded and two classes were held outside under the scanty shade of ancient acacia trees. Mrs. Ford, the head teacher, faced irate parents every day who wanted their children admitted to school. Everyone knew now that an uneducated child had no future; unskilled mine jobs for the men and back breaking farming for the girls. Mrs. Ford was strict and fair, managing her pupils and staff well, although she was exasperated at times with several of her male teachers whose thirst for alcoholic beverages made them slip away from their classes at unauthorized times. Kabo's teacher, Mrs. Dikgang, had children of her own of Kabo's age and was an enthusiastic and excellent teacher. The supple cane she carried and used frequently encouraged the wilder elements in the class to sit quietly. There was little equipment in the classroom, but each child did at least have a chair and a table shared with other children; Kabo was thankful for this because he knew of village schools where there were no chairs and the children even wrote their lessons with their fingers in the sand.

The walls of the classroom were decorated with posters and pictures—a framed photograph of His Excellency the President of Botswana dominated them all. Then there were pictures of the cabinet ministers, of Queen Elizabeth, of a London Park in the spring. There was a large Mine Labour Organization Calendar, metric conversion tables and the children's drawings of oxen, goats, and horses.

Kabo was good at arithmetic and already had his eye on a degree in engineering. His English too was fast improving, helped by Mrs. Dikgang's frequent use of the English language in her lessons. One day on the way home from school he met one of the British volunteers and proudly said to him, 'Good afternoon, sir,' but the volunteer was learning setswana and disappointed the surprised Kabo by replying, '*Dumela ngwanaka*'.

At play time Kabo and the other boys played football using an old tennis ball. Their bare feet were nimble and quick and they could kick really hard when the goal posts were near. Kabo knew that football was fast becoming the national game of Botswana, although tennis and golf were played by the more privileged people in Gaborone. Kabo hoped that one day he would play for one of the two Mole-polole teams, especially his favourite team, the Tigers, although many of the boys preferred the other team, *Masit-laoka*. He would be centre forward and play against other Botswana teams such as the Pirates, and the National Stadium in Gaborone would ring to the shouts of excited people as he drove the ball hard between the goal posts. The snag was that there always seemed to be quarrels amongst the national teams in the league and a lot of jealousy, but one day that would all be sorted out and he would go with a Botswana team to Europe and play before the great crowds there. In the meanwhile the tennis ball sufficed and the bare stony ground was a good preparation for the grassy fields of Europe!

The evenings were often dull for Kabo, just sitting round the fire after supper. It was all right when Thuto was in a talkative mood, telling tales of the old days or discussing the latest gossip of the village; but at other times the dark evenings dragged.

Every now and again there would be a concert in the community centre; or a dance would be organized with a band from Gaborone playing the latest pop songs with their electric guitars. Once a year the beauty contest would be held, when a dozen or so of the town's most attractive girls would parade before a panel of judges. The winner would proceed to the final competition in London—although in recent years the Botswana Council of Women which ran the contest had been unable to raise the necessary funds. Kabo liked the girl guide concert, held once or twice a year for camp funds. Admission was 10 thebe for a child and 20 thebe for an adult, and Kabo had little difficulty in persuading Thuto to give him the admission fee. Kabo always had a feeling of pride as he pushed through the crowd of shouting children milling round the door without admission money. The guides usually asked a Scouter, Mr. Busang, to act as chairman, and he sat at a small table beneath the platform with a huge bell which he rang at frequent intervals to try to keep some semblance of order. Kabo sat for an hour or so near the platform whilst the hall gradually filled up. The concert was scheduled to commence at 8 p.m., and at 9.15 p.m. the chairman, seeing that the hall was now filled to capacity, rang the bell and opened the evening's entertainment with a prayer, which on account of the shouting of children pressing at the windows and doors was scarcely audible, even though his voice was loud and resonant.

Nearly every function in Botswana is opened with a prayer, for all know that God is interested in everyday affairs. Thuto had told Kabo that the chief always asked one of his councillors to open the kgotla meetings with prayer, and Serwalo who had once with her classmates visited the National Assembly in Gaborone said that Speaker Lock always opened the daily meeting of Parliament with a prayer. Sometimes even things which God must surely not be happy about were opened with prayer, such as cafés where beer was sold; the beauty contest was always opened with a prayer.

The guide concert had some thirty items on the type-written programme—songs and sketches. Groups of girls had formed themselves into choirs—'The Heavenly Queens', 'The Brown Babies', 'The Molepolole Trio', and so forth. Each group when called by Mr. Busang sang loudly, enthusiastically, with dancing feet and swinging bodies. If the song was popular the whole audience roared approval. The programme went slowly, however, because frequently as soon as an item was commenced, some generous-hearted spectator would go forward and whisper in the chairman's ear. The bell would be rung loudly and when silence was obtained Mr. Busang would announce: 'Mr. Mooki has given 10 thebe and requests that the choir leave the platform and the next item on the programme be called.' Whereupon Miss Sellhako went forward and gave 25 thebe to Mr. Busang, saying, 'With this money I disagree; let the present item be finished.' Such interruptions went on all evening, so that after an hour had passed only some half dozen of the items on the programme had been heard; but no one minded, as this was how money was made. The more interruptions the more money! Kabo just wished that he had 25 thebe with which he could call the sketch forward which was billed half way down the programme as 'Sketch—The Wisdom of King Solomon'. He had seen it before, often in fact, as it was given at nearly all concerts. He knew that one of the senior guides, perhaps Dolly, would sit proudly dressed as King Solomon. He knew that he would see two of the guides, dressed as simple village women, sleeping with their babies. One of them would wake up and find her baby dead. She would shake it and cry and jump around the platform; then stealthily she would creep up to the other woman, still fast asleep and to the *tut tuts* of the excited audience she would replace her dead baby with the living one. Then morning would come and as the two women awakened, the evil one would sit quietly nursing her stolen baby. The poor deceived woman would cry in agony as she found her baby dead, until suddenly she would realize that it was not her baby, hers was in the arms of the evil woman! Then the quarrel—O the shouting, the pulling, the fighting of the two women, with the audience shouting abuse at the evil woman! Then to King Solomon for judgement. The verdict: 'Bring me a sword and I will divide the baby into two parts, one for each woman!' 'Oh no, no!' would cry the true mother, 'let her have the child!' Then the smile on the face of the King: 'You are the mother, take the child, it is yours.' And Kabo would shout his approval along with the rest of the audience.

At midnight the concert would end, whether the programme was finished or not. The money taken would be counted. Mr. Busang would ring the bell very loudly and then announce the grand total, perhaps 21 pula and 15 thebe. He would thank all who had come and then pronounce the Benediction. Kabo would push his way out through the noisy crowd and wind his way home along narrow lanes between darkened huts.

One evening at sunset Thuto and his small son Kabo were sitting by the fire watching Mmapula prepare the meal, when two Makgalagadi boys arrived driving a heavily laden, weary donkey before them. They wore skin trousers and their bodies were dust covered. Quietly, slowly, they squatted by the fire and respectfully greeted Thuto, who on seeing the donkey had groaned quietly to himself, realizing before the boys spoke what had happened. Across the donkey's back lay great pieces of meat, fly covered and already green in places. The old man did not return their greeting, merely looking at the boys and saying, 'Speak on, what do you say?'

'Father,' nervously ventured the elder of the two, 'your brown and white ox, the one with the broken horn, went missing a few days ago. We followed its footmarks for many hours through the bush until we found what the jackals had left.' Thuto groaned again. He knew the ox, a fine fat beast, one of his best. He and the boys went out to the donkey and Thuto groaned again, as a man would groan when he had lost something very near to his heart, for he recognized the skin at once. That night the men of the kgotla ate the meat, cooked in large three-legged pots, and what they left the women and children ate.

'Tomorrow, Friday, you can miss school, Kabo, and Monday is a holiday; we shall go to the cattle post and see what these Makgalagadi are up to.'

They set off at sunrise. Thuto walked with steady, slow step, old army greatcoat over his shoulder and stick in hand; the three boys ahead, taking it in turn to ride the donkey. The dogs trotted with them, sniffing the cold air for the scent of hares or guinea fowl. The first few miles followed a rough waggon road, sandy and rocky, flanked on each side by thorn scrub. Each boy carried a catapult with which he tried unsuccessfully to kill doves and partridges. Towards midday the country opened out into vast flat grassland interspersed with rugged camel thorn trees and thickets of thorn bush. They passed deserted farms, huts closed, the people back in Molepolole, while the cattle grazed on the mealie stumps.

The red ball of the sun was just disappearing as the boys reached the cattle post. Darkness would follow quickly. A couple of roughly thatched huts, windowless, surrounded by a thick fence of thorn bush, made up the cattle post. Nearby was the cattle kraal, a circle of thorn bush in which the cattle were already enclosed. Manure was piled high in the kraal. An old Makgalagadi servant of Thuto's was blowing twigs into a flame to make a fire for the evening meal. Thuto arrived soon after the boys, tired, dusty and hungry, for he had eaten nothing all day. The boys gave him a seat by the fire and the old servant brought him an enamel basin full of fresh milk, from which (after removing a few flies and ants) he drank deeply. The boys made a pot full of porridge, and as the cold of the night descended the fire drew all to its warmth. The four talked softly as they ate their porridge; the old servant gave Thuto all the news—of the cattle, and of the men who lived at their cattle posts around this area. A bore-hole had broken down some distance away and the farmers from that area were watering their cattle at Thuto's well. A goat had been eaten by a jackal. The veterinary people came a week ago to inspect the cattle for foot and mouth disease. In the background they heard, with silent pleasure, the soft stamp of the cattle as they chewed the cud, the bleat of goats, the distant dancing of herd boys and the far off plaintive cry of jackals.

Thuto did not sleep that night for his heart was full of fear. He had seen something that might be bad, the work of evil people. As he came through the opening in the thorn bush hedge he noticed in the loose sand a footprint, a man's footprint with widespread toes; there was only one for it appeared that the rest had been wiped out in the sand. It was a footprint he did not recognize, and he knew most of the footmarks of the farmers in that area. He could not place it but it reminded him of a distant relative of his, one Rramontsho, a tall man who had a cattle post some eight miles away. Then at the door of his hut, where the floor was smeared smooth and hard, he noticed a round mark, a stain of some sort, perhaps of some liquid which had been spilt there; but before he had really thought about it he passed over it and entered his hut. It was only then that he realized the danger he was in. That stain spoke of witchcraft, of powerful medicine placed there to bewitch and kill him as he entered his hut. He knew he had enemies around, men who were jealous of his wealth in cattle, sheep and goats, men who would gladly be rid of him, men who smiled and talked with him in the day time but at night became *baloi* (witches) with dark evil power. With sorcery they could enter huts, put the occupants into a deep sleep whilst they injected poison or extracted blood; with sorcery they could place medicine in the paths of unsuspecting people who passing over would be made ill. With their sorcery they could open locked huts and so beat people that they would wake up in the morning with sore limbs and painful heads. They could make people ill so that even if they went to Merriweather's hospital the doctors there would be unable to diagnose or treat the illness; for illness caused by witchcraft could only be cured by strong medicine of the traditional doctors.

Thuto feared Rramontsho more than all others. This dark-complexioned man had a fierce jealous nature and a bad temper. After terrorizing several wives with years of beatings before finally sending them away he had settled down with a tall scraggy woman whose vicious tongue and evil temper were a match for those of her husband. When he walked through the village, or along the tracts between cattle posts and farms, with his proud gait, his little white beard sticking out, his dark eyes flashing, people would drop their eyes, walk past him with humble greetings, and then in frightened whispers tell of his powers of sorcery and of his evil doings. And as the years went by his exploits of evil were exaggerated and people feared him more and more. He was not a herbalist who could mix concoctions to help sick people, nor would his bones of divination ever be used to bring comfort to people. His was to send lightning to strike huts; to send snakes to bite innocent people; to cause accidents and to cause bitter quarrels in family circles. Altogether evil! Thuto knew that he had recently been around his own cattle post area. Old Kgosie-mang had told Thuto that Rramontsho had some weeks back gazed with envy at Thuto's fat cattle and had muttered something about having those cattle when Thuto was dead. Thuto never really knew the truth about Rramontsho; perhaps it was that given a bad name a man was always regarded as bad. Now all night in his fitful sleep the face of Rramontsho kept appearing before him. It seemed to be glaring at him with an evil leer. He knew that there was only one way to find out if that spot on the floor was of evil significance or not, and that was to send for his own traditional doctor, old Kgotlayame, a doctor of good repute whose cattle post was not far away. Before sunrise he rose, wakened Kabo and told him to run with all speed to Kgotlayame's place and ask the doctor to come at once.

Kabo and the doctor arrived back when the red ball of the sun was just a hand's breadth above the horizon. Kabo could certainly run, and the old doctor was quite breathless as he arrived dressed in his old army coat to protect his thin bones from the early morning chill. His trousers were of stembuck skin, his shirt of khaki material while on his head was a jackal-skin hat. Thuto explained his predicament. Was the spot of evil significance or not? Was he already bewitched by it or were his fears ungrounded? The doctor squatted down outside the hut door, facing the spot, his right leg extended according to custom. Thuto, Kabo and the two Makgalagadi boys sat with him. From a snake skin bag the doctor took out his bones of divination. He held the bones in his hands, placed them to his lips blowing softly on them; then he threw them to the ground in front of him. All gazed in silence as the doctor began to handle them, point to them, speak to them. His four main bones were there, lying together, made from a calf's hoof, ankle bones of a sheep and a goat, and a bone from an ant bear. These were supported by less important bones, and the doctor knew from the way the bones fell and their relationship one with the other what they indicated. The bones had names—'god', 'old man', 'old woman' 'young man' and so forth. There were over sixty combinations of the four main bones that the doctor could study before he made any pronouncement. After a time he gathered the bones together and gave them to Thuto, who breathed on them and threw them down. Again the doctor studied them, talked to them, pleaded with them, calling them 'eyes that see'. Finally he turned to Thuto, his expression one of relief:

'The spot on your doorstep does not indicate anything evil. It is harmless. It is not placed there by witchcraft. It is paraffin spilt by one of your servants. You will not become ill. Rest assured; be at peace.'

Thuto smiled and thanked him. He also believed him.

An hour later Thuto stood at the entrance to his cattle kraal gazing with loving eyes at his forty oxen, his wealth which he would one day leave to his children who would call him blessed. Nothing touched his heart so much as cattle and he knew that every Motswana felt as he did; no sight on earth could give such pleasure as a long line of cattle coming slowly home to the kraal at sunset. The white people could have their bank accounts, they could be stirred as they thought of their wealth accumulating in the bank, but cattle were greater than money. They were living wealth, wealth that spoke of ancient customs, of marriages and funerals, of life in Botswana and tradition handed down from generation to generation. Cattle gave a man status, position, authority, respect. And Thuto knew each of his forty beasts, each oxen's colour, shape of horns and even its footprints. The language was rich in descriptive words for oxen; one word could describe a brown and white cow or a black ox, and at home one word would let

Kabo know that his father was referring to his spotted ox. Thuto remembered years ago when they had buried his own father just inside the cattle kraal, and in his heart he too hoped for such a burial; then a man's spirit would be at peace, for he would hear the cattle going out to graze each morning and hear the tramp of their feet as they returned safely in the evening. He doubted, however, that his children would bury him thus, for nowadays people were placed in the cold place at the hospital for a few days so that all the relatives could gather from far off places, and then a person could have a good funeral with speeches and prayers and be buried in the burial ground in the town. As he looked at his beasts, still fat and healthy at the end of the long dry winter, Thuto knew that not only did they speak to him of ancient custom and tradition but also of money. The abattoir at Lobatse gave good prices, for the outside world of South Africa, Zambia and Europe was hungry for meat and Botswana was exporting as much beef as she could, with the result that the people were saying, 'We are no longer poor; through our cattle industry we can obtain money to build proper houses, send our children to school and buy lorries and motor cars.'

Presently the boys appeared, having eaten their breakfast of mealie meal porridge. 'I will go out with the others and herd the cattle today,' announced Kabo. Thuto was glad that Kabo was developing a real farmer's love for cattle and the land, and he just hoped that the education he was giving him would not take that love from him. Kabo and the two Makgalagadi boys followed the cattle as they wound their way in single file through some thick thorn scrub and then out into the far stretching grassy plains where yellow dry grass, like hay, gave good grazing. The sun was up and rising rapidly; Kabo knew that the day would be long and tiring but there was much to see, much to occupy the boys as they quietly followed the grazing beasts. Bird life was everywhere; they startled a group of guinea fowl which flew swiftly away, but not before one of the boys had brought one down with his catapult; a serious looking secretary bird stalked angrily away as the boys approached its resting place; hawks floated effortless overhead; shrikes with brilliant red breasts flitted in the thorn bushes. Around midday a honey bird came to them leading them with its shrill and persistent cry to a crop of limestone where there was a bees' nest. The boys gratefully ate of the honey and when they had finished the bird engorged itself. All the time the sharp eyes of the boys looked for edible fruit, but their luck was out, the many wild fruit trees were barren as the rains had not yet come. They came upon a thickly barked tree and cut into its trunk with their sharp knives so that thick edible sap oozed out, delicious to hungry mouths. Now and again they disturbed a duiker or steenbok which leapt out of its thicket, dogs in hot pursuit. When hunger really gripped them the boys caught one of the goats and milked it straight into their mouths. All day as the cattle grazed the boys watched the sun which was not only their timepiece but their compass as well, and when it began to descend and the dark shadows grew longer they knew it was time to return. The cattle must be watered before being enclosed in their thorn bush kraal. When the boys reached the bore-hole, not far from their cattle post, they found a great mass of cattle, milling around, desperate for water. The men and boys were orderly, however, each man keeping back his beasts with his long lashing whip until their time for drinking came. It was after sunset before Kabo and his friends could water their beasts. They arrived home weary, but Kabo was satisfied. He had been a man today, he had herded cattle as his father and father's father had done for generations. He was a true Motswana and he felt a sense of pride, of achievement. This was the true life of Africa, to be a farmer.

Next day one of the Makgalagadi boys walked home to Molepolole with Kabo. Thuto stayed on for another week at the cattle post. Each morning and evening he gazed lovingly and proudly at his herd, his eyes feasting upon them, his heart at peace.

THE CIRCLE OF LIFE

FIVE YEARS LATER OLD Thuto passed over to his fathers. The end came suddenly. He went to bed early one evening saying that he had a pain in his chest and a nasty painful cough. All night he was ill and restless and Mmapula sat with him rubbing his chest with Vick's liniment. At the second cock crow he was delirious and said he could see his fathers and uncles calling him to the land beyond. His body shook with the rigours and high fever. Mmapula noticed that his spit was bloodstained and that his heart was beating rapidly in his chest and he could hardly breathe. She called Serwalo who was off that night and happened to be at home.

'Tomorrow, early, I will call Merriweather to come and see him', said Serwalo. But before the cocks brought in the new day, before dawn, when one could just see the horns of the cattle silhouetted against the sky, Thuto gave a few gasps and passed away. Just before he died he said, 'Let there be peace in my family.' Mmapula gave several shrieks and then sat back on her haunches, moaning softly. The household and neighbours hearing the cry knew that death had come and quickly came to sit with Mmapula in the hut of death. Serwalo also gave a loud cry, threw herself on the ground, crying bitterly, and then came to sit with the other people. Kabo hid his grief and said to himself, 'Now I must be a man and take my father's place.' The message was quickly passed round the kgotla and soon the courtyard was filled with mourners. One ran swiftly to the chief's place and said to Mokwena, '*Ke latola Thuto*', which meant, 'Thuto is no more.' When the post office opened, a telegram was sent to Mosetsanagape at the University in Gaborone and she arrived home that evening. Dineo suckling her third child was called in from the lands together with uncles and other relatives.

Thuto was not buried at his cattle post as he would have liked; he was given a funeral worthy of a sub-chief and a respected member of the tribe. He died on Wednesday and in order that all relatives could arrive, even those working in Johannesburg, the body was placed in the mortuary at the hospital and preparations made for Saturday. A funeral could last most of the day, for it was important to honour the dead, especially people like Thuto. There would be a service at the home with many speeches, and then at the grave; but Thuto would not be taken to the church because he had never confessed to be a Christian. However, because of Mmapula's status he would be given a Christian burial.

Soon after he died Mmapula's deacon arrived, hymn book and Bible in hand to conduct a short service, the first of many that would be held until the funeral and for a week afterwards; morning and evening ministers and deacons would perform that comforting duty. The deacon announced a hymn which spoke of Beulahland, written by Robert Moffat over a hundred years ago. As most people did not have hymn books the deacon skilfully called out the next line as each line finished. Then he read from John's gospel: 'In my Father's house are many mansions.' His prayer was long and very sincere, and he took the opportunity to sermonize a little as he prayed:

O Lord God, without beginning and without end,
Mighty Creator, King of Kings, greatest Lord,
You have promised to wipe away all our tears
And comfort our hearts.
We are gathered here today in this courtyard of mother Mmapula;
Not of our own will are we gathered; it is your will, you have
    called us.
If you call, what can we sinful mortals do?
We are made of flesh and blood, and you have given life.
You give and you take away.
We cannot complain. We say your will is best.
We thank you for the life of our father Thuto.
He was a good Mokwena; he was a faithful headman;
He helped the tribe in many ways.
He sent his children to school, so that now they are educated.

Receive his soul into everlasting peace, O God.
Here are his wife and family. They weep.
Comfort them, for you are the God of all comfort.
Look after them, for they are lost orphans; provide for their
every need.
Help us all to remember that the way Thuto has gone
Is our way. We cannot escape that road and we must go it alone.
Let us each prepare himself for entering the door of death.
For if we believe, it is the door of life.
We ask this in our Lord's Name. Amen.

Preparations for the funeral went smoothly, for there were three full days in which to arrange a programme, choose speakers and buy a worthy coffin. The days had gone when one could wrap the deceased in a blanket or make a coffin from planks bought at the Indian shop. There was an undertaker in Gaborone, and one of the family went to see him about the coffin and the artificial green grass which he must bring to the funeral. The deacons were kept very busy; morning and evening they came to pray and exhort the gathered people. Women sat for long hours with Mmapula, for at a time like this one needs other people for support. Black material was bought at Jalal's and dresses of deep mourning quickly sewn together. An ox and several goats were slaughtered, for there would be many hungry mourners. Numerous women helped with the making of scones and porridge, and day after day tea was brewed for the mourners who came and went all day long.

On Friday Mmapula and the children, with many mourners, sat up all night. This was the wake, and hymns were sung and the Bible read all through the long night. Person after person prayed and Mmapula was greatly comforted in her soul. Early on Saturday the undertaker arrived bringing a most beautiful, highly polished coffin with him. It had gilt handles and a lid which opened, allowing the mourners to file past and gaze for the last time on the kind face of Thuto. During the service in the courtyard the coffin was placed on two chairs, and the minister preached with great evangelical fervour. There was a long procession of cars and lorries following the hearse to the burial ground, for people had come in large numbers from Gaborone. At the grave another large crowd of people was waiting and Mmapula noted with pride that the chief himself was there, but she maintained an expression of sorrow, only glancing round furtively every now and again to see the crowds. The hole was deep, nearly seven feet, to ensure that no wild animal or witch could disturb Thuto. When the minister reached the words in his service book *dust to dust, ashes to ashes* a nephew of Thuto held out a spade full of soil and the minister sprinkled soil on the coffin. Mmapula and all the mourners did the same, for all were Thuto's children. Hymn after hymn was announced, some from the Congregational book and some from the Anglican book. After everyone had sprinkled a little soil on the coffin, several men grabbed spades and proceeded to fill in the grave. Clouds of fine dust rose into the air and those on the windward side were soon covered with it. All the soil that had been removed was replaced and piled up on the grave, held in position by large stones placed round the outside. There were several speeches in which representatives of various groups of people spoke and eulogized about Thuto. The chairman then read out letters and telegrams that had been received and announced who had sent wreaths and what message they had placed on the wreath. The closing hymn was a sad one with a refrain 'Greetings, my loved one' sung after each verse, and at the closing verse the singing crowd stretched out hands in salute saying goodbye to Thuto.

After the burial service the people walked back to Thuto's place or climbed on to the back of trucks that were heading that way. The men assembled in the kgotla, the women in the courtyard, waiting the announcement that would officially pronounce Thuto dead and buried. An old man announced to the men, and an old woman to the women: 'Thuto is dead, we have buried him, and now we poor dogs remain.'

The evening was taken up with eating, for it was no light matter to feed over two hundred people! Mmapula was not left alone; women slept with her each night and sat with her during the days. For a whole week she was sustained by the prayers and the preaching of the deacons. Gradually the sympathy and presence of so many friends took her sorrow away. But for many weeks a woman slept with her, for loneliness after bereavement can break the heart, while a companion can comfort and console.

A couple of weeks after the funeral two of Thuto's brothers visited Mmapula. They were doubtful if their mission would succeed in view of Mmapula's strong convictions, but they thought it worth a try:

'Your husband has died,' began the elder after the usual preliminary greetings and discussion about the weather. 'You know there is our custom of *boshwagadi*, cleansing of the widow. When the time is ready we shall bring a good and powerful doctor to perform this rite on you.' Mmapula's reply was as they expected: 'Some of our customs are good and helpful and we should honour them. We have our African ways, many of which are good and of which we can be proud, but this you are asking me to do goes back to ignorant superstition and heathen witchcraft. I will have nothing of it. It is against my Christian faith.'

The men knew that they could never move her on this. So the younger spoke also. 'Mother, we are not happy about Thuto's death. It came so suddenly and unexpectedly and really it was without cause. We fear it was the work of an enemy through sorcery. We propose to call a doctor to *tlhapisa phupu*, to wash the grave with medicine so that those responsible for his death will also die.' Mmapula knew this custom well; it was often done. Indeed one of the so-called Christian prophets in Molepolole used to do it for people, mixing up old heathen customs with his brand of Christianity. Mmapula's reply was as the men expected: 'My husband has gone to God. I want no revenge. I am satisfied that God's will has been done.'

The men went away, annoyed and impotent in the face of Mmapula's strong convictions.

Mmapula wore her black dress for a full twelve months. That was the period of mourning. She had shaved her head after the funeral as custom demanded but she refused further attempts on the part of some of her elders to be cleansed by the witchdoctor. She washed Thuto's clothes and packed them away in a suitcase. After a year they would be divided out amongst the family and Thuto's brothers and uncles would distribute the cattle and small stock according to setswana custom. In the meanwhile she had no regrets, she had been an obedient wife, giving him children, looking after the home and farm, and she had given him a good funeral. She would continue in her church activities and she would be respected as the widow of an important man.

Serwalo's marriage had worked out well. She was now a member of the church, as befitted the wife of a respectable church-going civil servant, and she already had two children, a girl called Neo (meaning 'gift') and a boy Morongwa (which means 'messenger'). She had been posted to Serowe hospital where she was a senior nurse gaining much valuable experience and able to take responsibility. Her husband was unfortunately still in Gaborone, being unable to persuade the ministry to transfer him to Serowe. They had little home life together, but that was usual because educated men married educated women and both wanted to work, with the result that they were often separated. At the weekends Peter would sometimes manage a trip to Serowe, and when she was off duty for a few days Serwalo would visit Gaborone. At times she became uneasy, for Gaborone was full of young women who had drifted there looking for work. She did not ask questions, indeed she did not really suspect Peter, and her mother had often warned her that great patience was needed to make a marriage successful, and that men were very different from women. They had a house, rented from the Government in Gaborone, and they had begun to build their own house in Molepolole not far from Peter's kgotla. It was to have brick walls, a corrugated iron roof and several rooms.

Her two children had been left in the care of Mmapula who accepted her lot of bringing up her second family as quite a natural thing to do. The little ones were well cared for and very happy and did not seem to mind seeing their parents only at weekends or at holiday times. Serwalo was happy enough. Many girls had missed marriage and were always ready prey for men. She had status, she had money for clothes and she bought only the very best, nothing cheap. She and Peter were determined that their children would be well educated. After some discussion Peter had agreed that they should limit their family to four so that they could clothe them and educate them well.

Mosetsanagape had done well. Her early determination had borne fruit. She had passed her O-levels and was now in Gaborone doing a B.Sc. degree before going on to study medicine. She was still very religious; her whole life was sustained by her faith. She was secretary of the University Student Christian Movement. Her outspoken faith was a source of amusement to many of her colleagues, many of whom regarded the Christian faith as 'foreign propaganda'. She had grown into a lovely, attractive girl of whom her mother was now more proud than ever. She was intelligent and could hold her own in all the discussions which went on in the University. The male students respected her and com- plained at times that her sexual morality was too strict and old-fashioned. She was determined to do well and she would be ready for marriage when the right man approached her. Botswana needed doctors and her great aim was to finish her medical course. She had seen other African women at Princess Marina Hospital who were fully qualified doctors, hard working and well spoken of by their patients. If they could do it, so could she. The Government had promised her a bursary to study in Nairobi or Lagos. She had a bright future ahead.

Kabo was now doing Junior Certificate at the secondary school. He was a joy to his widowed mother. He was studious, quiet and well mannered. He was good with his hands and was keen to become an engineer. What really delighted his mother was the fact that he was still a keen farmer and at every opportunity went out to the cattle post to see how things were going there. Mmapula noticed with relief that he had not yet started to go out at night in search of drink and women. Each evening he went to the secondary school where he could do his homework in brightly lit classrooms. Sundays, when he did not go to the cattle post, found him at the Bible class, and Mmapula's joy was full when one day he said to her, 'Today at the Bible class I gave myself to Christ. I am a Christian.' She now believed with all her heart that her last born child and only son would bring her joy in her old age.

So in contentment and peace Mmapula's circle of life went on. Ploughing time came each year, the trek out to the lands, the sowing, followed by the hoeing until hands were blistered, the long days chasing birds away, the harvesting of beans, mealies and corn, then the threshing and the homeward trek. The church services, the women's meeting, the dressing up in church uniform—white blouse and black skirt, the bringing up of her grandchildren, the smearing of house and courtyard with mud and cow dung. This was life, a life of contentment with simple things. And her children respected her, educated though they may be. They loved to come home to visit her and they would buy her shoes, material for dresses, sugar and tea. Dineo, the one with many children who had missed education, was happy in her own home, in her own farm, living like her mother the simple life of the people of Botswana. Mmapula thought often of her family and thanked God for each of them—for Dineo, simple and hard working like herself; for Serwalo, who had given her much anxiety and who now looked after her well; for Mosetsanagape, her pride and joy, the serious one, the religious one to whom her heart seemed to turn more than any of the others; and for Kabo, the boy who would take his father's place and upon whom she would rely more than anyone else for the comforts of old age.

In the meanwhile there were her grandchildren to look after . . . a woman's work was never ending.